Early Keyboard Instruments

The Benton Fletcher Collection at Fenton House

Early Keyboard Instruments

Mimi S. Waitzman

 THE NATIONAL TRUST

First published in Great Britain in 2003

National Trust Enterprises Ltd
36 Queen Anne's Gate
London
SW1H 9AS
www.nationaltrust.org.uk

ISBN 0-7078-0353-5

Cataloguing in Publication Data is available from the British Library

Designed by Fetherstonhaugh Associates
www.fetherstonhaugh.com

Printed in Hong Kong by Wing King Tong Ltd

Photograph, page 1: Major Benton Fletcher with Mrs Arthur Chorley, playing the Vincentius virginals (no.5) at the Queen Elizabeth Loan Exhibition, c.1936.
Photograph, page 2: detail of the keywell of the Italian harpsichord (no.15), showing the remaining carved cherub and the divided or split accidental keys in the bass.

Contents

Acknowledgements

The National Trust and the author gratefully acknowledge the gift from the David Cohen Trust which has made possible the publication of this book.

The book's realisation has also been facilitated by the generous help of many colleagues and friends. Among them, I am most greatly indebted to Christopher Nobbs for his superb drawings, and his many insightful suggestions which improved the text. I am equally obliged to Andrew Garrett for the exceptional care he took in reading and discussing the text with me, and to Richard Ireland for his invaluable assistance in the preparation of the technical data. Special thanks are offered to John Hammond whose outstanding photographs capture the instruments and myriad details with exquisite clarity. Photographs of the Ruckers harpsichord (no.2) are reproduced by gracious permission of Her Majesty The Queen. Grant O'Brien has kindly permitted aspects of his research on Celestini and his attribution of the virginals (no.18) to be released here in advance of its general publication. Derek and Elizabeth Jackson very generously allowed personal photographs to be reproduced and freely shared their knowledge and archival material. I am also grateful to Tony Bingham who gave me access to books in his personal collection and permitted the Longman & Broderip business card to be reproduced. For the helpful contributions and information they provided, I would also like to thank: Augustine Ford, Derek Adlam, Darryl Martin, Miles Hellon, Grant O'Brien, Denzil Wraight, Peter Bavington, David Hunt, John Barnes, Kenneth Mobbs, and Nigel Hill. Virginia Murray of John Murray Publishers (London) generously allowed the reproduction of the photograph of the Dolmetsch family gathered around the clavichord. Maurice Cochrane, Ian Harwood and John Stewart Morley very kindly helped me to complete Appendix II. Of all the specialist catalogues consulted, John Koster's on the Keyboard Collection at the Boston Fine Arts Museum should be mentioned as perhaps the most indispensable and inspirational. Thanks are also extended to Anthea Palmer, Jonathan Marsden and Linden Williams who combed National Trust archives in pursuit of answers to (sometimes arcane) questions, and to Lisa Vaughan, who read the text with a non-specialist's eye and offered many helpful suggestions. I am immensely thankful to Susan Alcock for liaising with the David Cohen Trust, and for her unwavering faith and timely reassurance. My editors, Ruth Thackeray and James Parry, simply cannot be thanked enough. Any errors which may remain are entirely mine. Finally, I am deeply grateful to my husband, Donald Mackinnon, who gave unflagging encouragement and support throughout the long gestation of this book.

Author's Note

This book has been written primarily for visitors to Fenton House and for non-specialists as an introduction to the history and context of the Benton Fletcher Collection of Early Keyboard Instruments. To appreciate this fully, a certain amount of musical background and specialist technical knowledge is of course helpful. For those who wish to know more than it has been possible to include here, the bibliography may serve as a point of departure. Terms that may be new to non-specialists are explained in the glossary and are indicated the first time they appear in each section of the text through the use of capital letters, as in DOGLEG COUPLER (entered under D, not C).

To facilitate the use of this book by visitors, the instruments are listed in the order in which they appear in Fenton House if the rooms on each floor are visited clockwise, that is beginning on each floor with the room immediately on one's left. When an instrument can be heard on the accompanying CD, the corresponding track number(s) appear(s) at the end of its entry before the technical data.

Pitch notation conforms to that shown on the following staves:

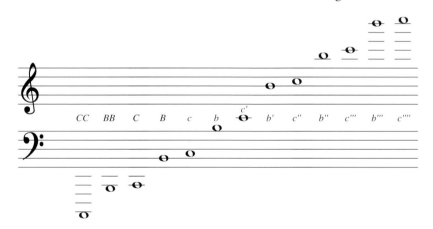

In the text, the term 'eight-foot' (8') refers to a concept of normal pitch. Adopted from organ terminology, 8' indicated that the length of the pipe for the note *C* measured about eight feet. Therefore, the pitch at which *C* and all its companion pipes in that stop sounded (whatever their length) was called 8' pitch.

A 'four-foot' (4') stop (with pipes theoretically half the length) would sound the notes an octave higher, and a 16' stop would sound the notes an octave lower. Although the 'normal pitch' of historic keyboard instruments varied from today's standard ($a' = 440$Hz) by a tone or more, both higher and lower, the relationship among 8', 4', 16' and 2' pitches obviously remains constant.

No microscopic analysis of woods has been undertaken for this book, nor has there been any systematic attempt to identify and record the materials from which the instruments are made. Any wood which is named has been identified by sight or knowledge of usual practice, and must therefore be considered a botanical uncertainty. In every instance we have endeavoured to give at least as much of this type of information as has been given in previous Fenton House guidebooks which, unless clearly erroneous, have served as the main source for most of the wood identifications.

Because this volume aims particularly to engage non-specialists, introductory, explanatory, historical and contextual information and drawings and photographs have taken precedence over technical data. Nevertheless, a critical minimum is included and represents not only far more than has ever been available previously, but also the first step towards an extended technical documentation of the collection. This information appears in a box at the end of each instrument entry. All measurements are in millimetres, to the nearest millimetre. The plucking points of each of the virginals are measured from the left-hand bridge. The case measurements exclude lids and mouldings unless otherwise indicated. The width of harpsichords and pianos is measured at the lower edge in front of the keyboard; the depth, at the keyboard end of the spine. The word 'lines' is used to refer to the thin ornamental banding surrounding veneered panels, rather than the potentially confusing term 'stringing'. The '3-octave span' is the width of the 21 naturals *F–e''*. The registers of harpsichords are shown in the widely accepted manner: a plan view of the gap from the keyboard end, with arrows indicating the direction in which each register engages. All the soundboard roses in the photographs are circular, but appear slightly oval because of the angle from which the pictures were taken.

Above all, the author would ask that this book be regarded as a work in progress. Where the documentation of a collection is discontinuous, sketchy or lacking integration, as it is in the Benton Fletcher Collection, a complete image is assembled in unexpected ways: often by following a trail of anecdotes, or even apparently unrelated paths. Research is bringing new information to light all the time and it is hoped that this, along with more complete technical data, may be reflected in future publications or editions.

Introduction

George Henry Benton Fletcher (1866–1944), Collector

The understanding and appreciation of early music is greatly enhanced by performance on period instruments. This view, although widely espoused today, was regarded as quaint to the point of eccentricity when Major George Henry Benton Fletcher began his instrument collection in the early decades of the twentieth century.

Despite the scepticism of the musical mainstream, Benton Fletcher's conviction was shared by a small but growing number of collectors, musicians, scholars and instrument makers. Most influential among them in England were Arnold Dolmetsch and the clergyman F.W. Galpin, both of whom had strong musical backgrounds. Benton Fletcher, in contrast, had a panoply of interests, talents and careers. Born in 1866, he had served in the Boer War, become a social worker in south London and excavated at archaeological sites in Egypt alongside Flinders Petrie. He had illustrated an edition of Pepys's diaries, and always drew the historic artefacts and buildings that he encountered on his travels abroad. As a result, Major Fletcher's enthusiasm for early music differed from his better known contemporaries in at least two decisive respects: it was motivated by a more general concern for the preservation of all significant works of art; and it was sustained by a deep-rooted patriotism. These sympathies, whether expressed in a devotion to ancient music or to ancient monuments, were ones that found greater congruence in the fledgling National Trust movement than within the Arts and Crafts sphere of Dolmetsch, with whom he shared ostensibly similar aims. Indeed, Major Fletcher's acquaintance with two of the founders of the National Trust, Miss Octavia Hill and Sir Robert Hunter[1], undoubtedly helped galvanise his impulse to collect. Scorning modern reproductions, he set about finding significant examples of authentic early keyboard instruments. Having them restored, played and heard then became his consuming passion.

From Benton Fletcher's point of view, such a collection required an appropriate setting and ambience in which to be appreciated fully. In 1934,

George Henry Benton Fletcher as a young officer. He rose to the rank of Major and saw active service in South Africa.

Benton Fletcher in Arab dress, seated in front of his drawing of Islam's holy city of Mecca, in 1934.

in pursuit of this ideal, he purchased Old Devonshire House in London's Bloomsbury, a medium-sized seventeenth-century aristocratic residence that had fallen into disrepair. A blacksmith, who kept a working forge in the cellar, was among the tenants who had to be persuaded to vacate the premises before Benton Fletcher could begin to return the house to its former appearance and domestic function. Following its restoration, he installed himself with his growing collection of early keyboard instruments. A letter

A letter in Benton Fletcher's own hand, to the Friends of Music Society, dated 12 April 1937. See App. III for transcript of the text.

from Benton Fletcher to the Friends of Music Society, exhibited in the South-West Attic at Fenton House and reproduced above, outlines many of his plans and aspirations[2]. Although he clearly sought and enjoyed the company of like-minded people, Major Fletcher presumably also prized his independence, for throughout his life he remained wedded only to his work and his collecting.

Very little of the provenance of the various instruments or their restoration history is documented. Most of the instruments were probably acquired at auction, although Benton Fletcher was fond of recounting how he found the Celestini virginals (no.18) in a cellar in Florence. It was being used as a carpenter's workbench and he had to brush out the wood shavings to see inside. One of the English bentside spinets (no.8) was unearthed in an outhouse in Wales, while the Longman & Broderip harpsichord (no.17), his first acquisition, was extracted from beneath several armchairs in a second-hand shop in Wells, Somerset. No receipts survive, but it is said that he never paid more than £20 for an instrument.

In 1937 Benton Fletcher gave Old Devonshire House and its contents to the National Trust. He was the first to take advantage of the National Trust Act of Parliament, allowing owners of historic houses to continue living in them as tenants once they had made over the freehold to the Trust. A catalogue by him, dated 1938, lists eighteen keyboard instruments: four virginals, two clavichords, two English bentside spinets (which he called transverse spinets), six harpsichords (all eighteenth-century English), two grand pianofortes and two pipe organs. Among the painted portraits of musical significance, which he also gave to the National Trust, were those of Samuel Pepys, John Blow, Henry Purcell, Daniel Purcell, J.C. Pepusch, G.F. Handel and Thomas Arne. Early printed musical scores and manuscripts were also included in the gift. By the outbreak of war in 1939, two more instruments, the single-strung Italian harpsichord (no.15), and the 'Backers' piano (no.13), had been added to the collection.

The war halted Major Fletcher's collecting. The concerts, teaching and open-air theatre performances – which had begun to attract the attention of music colleges and early music enthusiasts in London – also ceased. Benton Fletcher, in common with many owners of grand London houses, feared for the safety of his collections, and in January 1941 fifteen of the keyboard instruments were moved to a house in the Cotswolds. The transfer proved timely. In May of the same year, Old Devonshire House and its remaining contents, including paintings, furniture and, incidentally, the stands for the majority of the evacuated keyboard instruments, perished in an air raid.

It is believed that five instruments were lost in the raid: a sixteenth-century Italian clavichord, a grand piano by Matthew and William Stodart dated 1791, a grand piano by Joseph Kirckman dated 1803, a sixteenth-century portable Italian pipe organ and an English pipe organ inscribed 'Merlin, 1754'. These absent instruments lend an important insight into Major Fletcher's underlying concept for his collection. Clearly, instruments with struck actions, that is early pianos and clavichords, were to have been more fully represented, as were early organs.

Exhibited on the Attic landing at Fenton House is Benton Fletcher's drawing of the Queen Anne terraced house at 3 Cheyne Walk, which he and

Old Devonshire House in Boswell Street, London, the first home for the Benton Fletcher Collection.

Miss Cicely Burnaby Atkins, received by Major Benton Fletcher and Lady Geraldine Boyle as Lord and Lady Charles Cavendish at one of Major Fletcher's parties. On this occasion, all the guests dressed in strict Charles II costume in order to harmonise with the period of Old Devonshire House.

A drawing by Benton Fletcher of the house at 3 Cheyne Walk, acquired as a new home for the collection after Old Devonshire House was destroyed in the Second World War. Displayed at Fenton House on the Attic landing.

the National Trust purchased in 1943 as a new home for the instruments. There, the activities begun at Old Devonshire House were to continue. Benton Fletcher died in 1944 before this plan could be realised, but his intentions were fulfilled after the war by the National Trust. Students were invited to practise and concerts again took place. A certain continuity was maintained at the new location in the person of the Curator, Mrs Eileen Jackson, who had played an integral part in arranging and organising both the musical and practical sides of life in Devonshire House. Fortunately, she also kept a scrapbook of articles, letters, memoirs and newspaper cuttings by or about Benton Fletcher, which now comprises the principal source of information on the pre-National Trust years of the collection[3].

In 1948 Trinity College, the only London conservatory to have offered its students early keyboard lessons on the collection before the war, opened a department of sixteenth- and seventeenth-century music at the Chelsea address, in co-operation with the National Trust. The probate valuation of Benton Fletcher's estate lists sixteen keyboard instruments, fifteen of which form the core of the present collection.

In 1952 these instruments, together with Her Majesty The Queen's 1612 Ruckers harpsichord (no.2), were moved to the more spacious surroundings of Fenton House, where the indefatigable Mrs Jackson became the first Custodian. Her unflagging enthusiasm for Benton Fletcher's objectives ensured both their resolute perpetuation and a smooth transition to the

Hampstead location[4]. Since then the collection has been augmented by two Broadwood pianos (nos 12 and 14) and a Dolmetsch clavichord (no.10). As Benton Fletcher would have wished, early keyboard students still come to practise. A concert series held every year and occasional events – such as master classes, recordings and competitions – continue to make the collection a focal point for students and devotees of early music, not only locally, but nationally and internationally.

Below left: Fenton House, the third and present home of the collection.

Below: Mrs. Eileen Jackson, who had assisted Benton Fletcher with the collection at both Devonshire House and Cheyne Walk, was the first Curator of Fenton House. She is pictured here in the garden of the house.

The single-strung Italian harpsichord (no.15).

The keywell of the double-manual harpsichord by Jacob and Abraham Kirckman (no.6), showing the slender jackrail parallel to the 8' nut, covering the lute register jacks.

The Benton Fletcher Collection in Perspective

Very few keyboard instruments of any description made in England during the sixteenth and early seventeenth centuries survive[5]. Whatever the reasons for this, it is certain that indigenous musicians also acquired keyboard instruments from Italy and the Low Countries, the great centres of harpsichord making during this period. The Benton Fletcher Collection, considering its small size, includes a remarkable selection of extremely rare, or even unique sixteenth- or early seventeenth-century Italian examples. These, together with the 1612 Ruckers harpsichord (no.2) and the rare seventeenth-century English virginals (no.11), cast an important and informative light on the practice of music in England both before and during the eighteenth century.

Notwithstanding an English partiality, it is unlikely that Benton Fletcher acquired instruments expressly to trace the complicated transition from harpsichord to pianoforte in this country. Nevertheless, the collection, as it stands today, invites this interpretation. The six late eighteenth-century English harpsichords range from the elegantly simple to the exquisitely extravagant with all the accretions that herald the instrument's demise. The three English pianos in the collection (nos 12, 13 and 14), all of which fall within the period when harpsichords were still in production (Kirckman's last known harpsichord dates from 1809), reflect, both in structure and action, some of the important stages in the piano's development to 1805. Also well illustrated is the progress of the prominent Broadwood firm, from its founding in London by the harpsichord maker Burkat Tschudi (who later anglicised his name to Shudi), to its shift to piano manufacture under the guidance of his son-in-law, John Broadwood.

All collections require continual reappraisal and reinterpretation. It is refreshing to meet a set of objects which were gathered systematically, but not solely for any personality association, prestige, rarity or pecuniary value. Benton Fletcher prized these instruments simply for what they were, what they represented and what they could do. The idea that things of such unusual beauty and quality were regarded as ordinary in their own time captivated him. From reading his letters and articles, it is clear that he felt he was helping to rectify a colossal injustice by rescuing these instruments from neglect or oblivion. In his appreciation of their intrinsic worth, he was well in advance of most of his contemporaries.

Since the Second World War, musicians and instrument makers have drawn information and inspiration from this collection. Many prominent harpsichordists and harpsichord builders cite it as an important source for their initial interest. During the 1950s, 60s and 70s, when the early music revival was still considered new, Fenton House was one of the very few places where authentic early keyboard instruments could be heard and played. It remains so today. We may feel gratified that certain of these objects have attained a high status or monetary value in musical and other artistic communities. But nothing of their essence has changed since they were acquired. Only the context of the collection and the eyes that view it have changed.

Action Types

The three principal types of stringed keyboard instrument, HARPSICHORDS, CLAVICHORDS and PIANOS, are all represented in the collection. Benton Fletcher realised the intimacy of the relationship between a musical composition and the intended instrument's means of sound production. Just as piano music required the piano, music conceived for plucked instruments such as harpsichords, SPINETS or VIRGINALS required exactly the resources that they provided. These included an incisive attack and a clarity of line essential for the many-voiced contrapuntal style of the period.

Virginals, Spinets and Harpsichords

The idea of using a keyboard-operated mechanism to pluck strings dates from the late fourteenth century, and plucked keyboard instruments remained popular throughout the following four hundred years. Remarkably, the action's main components, elegant in their simplicity, changed very little during that time (see Figs 1 and 2). The heart of the action is the JACK, a rectangular slip of wood that stands upright on the distal end of the key. The jacks are arranged in rows called REGISTERS, and large instruments with four registers can have 240 or more jacks. At the top of each jack is a wide slot in which a wooden TONGUE is pivoted. The tongues hold fast the PLECTRA, which, usually made from cuttings from the shafts of quills, or occasionally from leather, extend beneath the strings. A spring, which could be made of a boar's bristle or thin metal leaf or wire, holds the tongue/plectrum unit forward so that when the key is depressed and the jack rises, the plectrum is forced past the string making it sound. When the key is released, the plectrum, on its way back down, comes to rest momentarily on the string, supporting the weight of the jack. This weight quickly causes the tongue to retract against its spring, allowing the plectrum

Fig. 1 *Example of a harpsichord action, based on a late sixteenth-century Italian harpsichord and showing all the fundamental elements of the jack action, except the spring (see Fig.2).*

a   *jack body*
b   *key*
c   *tongue*
d   *quill plectrum*
e   *string*
f   *cloth damper*
g   *balance rail*
h   *balance pin*
i   *register*
j   *jackrail*
k   *keyframe*
l   *rack (or rear guide for keys)*
m   *wooden guide fixed into the rear of the key*

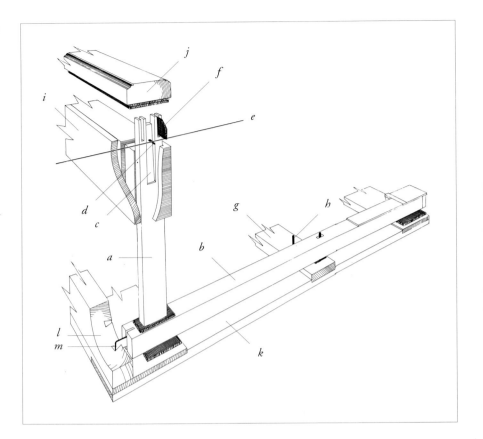

to escape or slip back under the string. The spring then pushes the tongue to its forward position with the plectrum under the string, ready to sound again. Finally, the DAMPERS, small flags of woollen cloth inserted in narrow slots at the top of the jacks, come to rest on the strings and damp the note (see Fig.2).

It is small comfort that earlier ages found the nomenclature of plucked keyboard instruments as troublesome and perplexing as we do. For example, during the seventeenth century in England all such instruments, regardless of shape, were called 'virginalls', but during the same period in France they were known as *épinettes*. Today, each of these words has acquired a precise technical definition, which antique instruments frequently confound. In this collection, all instruments in which the BRIDGE and NUT rest in whole or in part on free SOUNDBOARD, where the lowest (longest) string is the one nearest the player and the tuning pins are to one side, are called virginals. The shape of these may be rectangular or polygonal. Where the nut is mounted entirely on the WRESTPLANK, the lowest string is the one furthest from the player and the tuning pins are arrayed along the front, the instrument has been called

16

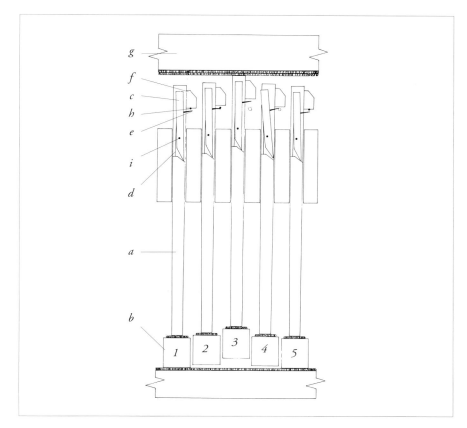

a   jack
b   key, viewed from rear
c   tongue
d   spring
e   plectrum
f   cloth damper
g   jackrail
h   string, in section
i   pivot

1   The jack and key are at rest, the tongue/plectrum unit is being held forward by the spring, and the cloth damper is in contact with the string.
2   The key is being depressed at the front, making the jack rise. The plectrum (held rigid in the tongue) begins to flex against the string. The damper leaves the string.
3   The key is fully depressed at the front (and fully raised at the back). The plectrum has been forced past the string which is now sounding (vibrating). The jack is stopped at the jackrail.
4   The key is released and both key and jack begin to fall. The tongue/plectrum unit comes to rest momentarily on the still vibrating string, supporting the weight of the jack. This weight forces the tongue/plectrum unit to retract against its spring, allowing the plectrum to escape (slip back) under the string.
5   The plectrum has now escaped under the string and the tongue/plectrum unit has been returned by the spring to its forward position, ready for the process of sounding to begin again. The damper has come into contact with the string, silencing it.

'spinet'. Although spinets can vary in appearance, the two in this collection (nos 7 and 8) are both of the eighteenth-century English bentside type, easily identified by their distinctive wing shape and handsome veneered cases. The remaining plucked keyboard instruments, all of which have contours suggestive of the modern grand piano, are called harpsichords.

While virginals and spinets usually possess a single set of strings, harpsichords may have one, two or three sets[6], each corresponding with one or more registers, or rows of jacks (see Figs 7 and 8). These registers, as in an organ, can be used individually or coupled, by means of hand stops, pedals or movable keyboards. Stops creating special effects of TIMBRE were popular on large and small instruments alike. Multiple keyboards also facilitated easily discernible contrasts in timbre and dynamic level, perhaps useful for delineating large sections of pieces or characterising different movements. Indications by Baroque composers for using these stops or for any changes in dynamics or timbre are very scarce. Their absence, together with the impossibility of producing gradations in dynamics in plucked actions simply by varying the force of touch, have given rise to the common misconception that such nuances were not necessary. In fact, accomplished players understood how to create an effective illusion of variety and dynamics through the appropriate use of touch, articulation, ornamentation and registration. In many ways the playing of single-register instruments demanded the greatest skill, for no extrinsic devices were available to help magnify and clarify the composers' intentions.

A vast solo and ensemble repertoire, spanning at least three and a half centuries, exists for pre-piano keyboard instruments. The earliest surviving solo music dates from the fourteenth century and consists of improvisations which were written down, INTABULATIONS or transcriptions of popular vocal pieces, dance music and divisions (variations). Later forms retained many vestiges of this inheritance and grew to include the toccata, the prelude and fugue, the fully developed dance suite, theme and variations and the sonata. The non-organ keyboard works of the celebrated eighteenth-century Baroque masters, J.S. Bach, G.F. Handel, François Couperin and J-P. Rameau, were composed, almost without exception, for harpsichord[7]. Although the piano was known to them, it was regarded, during most of their lives, as an intriguing experiment, with musical resources ill-matched to the contemporary aesthetic.

Much music for plucked keyboards would also have been played on the clavichord or organ. Indeed, most harpsichordists were first and foremost organists. But the orientation of the harpsichord was primarily secular, and its role in chamber music, whether within or outside an ecclesiastical setting, was literally fundamental. As a continuo instrument, often together with other low-pitched instruments, it provided not only the rhythmic but also the harmonic framework upon which the melodic parts relied. Even today, it is not generally appreciated that a harpsichord 'accompanist', rather like a modern jazz player, is actually improvising much of his part from a figured bass, a musical line with numbers indicating the harmonic progressions.

Clavichords

The clavichord, ordinarily rectangular in shape, was not only a predecessor and contemporary of plucked instruments, but also outlasted them in popularity in Germany and Scandinavia. Uniquely among keyboard instruments, it is not based on the principle of applying a keyboard to an existing non-keyboard instrument[8]. It has a struck action, as does a piano, but its strings are struck by blades of metal called TANGENTS, rather than by hammers. When a key is depressed (see Fig.3) the tangent, fixed on the distal

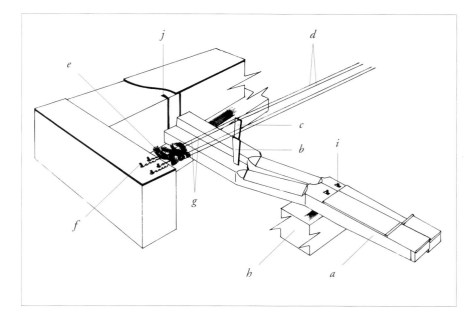

Fig. 3 *A clavichord action. The strings are struck by blades of metal called tangents (b and c). When a key (a) is depressed the tangent comes into contact with the set of strings (d) associates with that note, at once defining their sounding length and causing them to speak. The listing (e), a strip of woollen cloth woven among the strings, keeps the overlength of the strings (g) (the untuned portion from hitchpin (f) to tangent) from sounding when the tangent strikes. It also serve to damp the whole string once the key has been released. (For a fretted clavichord action, see Fig.11.)*

a   key
b   tangent and key at rest
c   tangent in contact with strings
d   string pair (or set), tuned or sounding portion
e   listing
f   hitchpin
g   string pair, overlength (untuned portion)
h   balance rail
i   balance pin
j   rear key guide slot

end of the key, comes into contact with the set of strings (usually, but not always, a pair of strings) associated with that note, at once defining their sounding length and causing them to speak. Because the string pair is activated on one of its end points and by a fixed (rather than a free-flying) agent, very little volume, compared with a harpsichord or piano, is generated. On the other hand, this same feature yields tones with a rich harmonic development. In addition, the player's direct contact with the string through the tangent allows him or her to produce not only touch-sensitive dynamics, impossible on the harpsichord, but also subtle expressive effects such as vibrato, which are impossible on any other stringed keyboard instrument. The LISTING, a strip of woollen cloth woven among the strings, keeps the overlength of the strings (that portion from hitchpin to tangent) from sounding when the tangent strikes. It also serves to damp the whole string once the key has been released.

When the sounding length of two or more adjacent notes is created by their tangents striking at different points along only one pair (or set) of strings, the clavichord is said to be fretted (see Fig.11). Unfretted instruments, where each note possessed its own pair or set of strings, gradually superseded the earlier fretted type.

The clavichord filled many functions throughout its long history, due in equal part to the extraordinary finger discipline required to play it well, its compact structure and its soft but versatile tone. It was used for composing

The anonymous triple-fretted clavichord (no.19). Note the cranking of the keys and the positioning of the tangents necessary to accomplish the fretting. The red cloth is the listing. See also Fig.11.

(even into the nineteenth century) and teaching, and as a convenient practice instrument for organ, harpsichord and even piano music. Additionally, during the mid- to late eighteenth century in Germany, a small but significant solo repertoire was composed specifically for the clavichord. The instrument's poetic effects and range of dynamic nuance both served and inspired a pre-Romantic style of composition, intimate, sentimental and intensely personal, known as *empfindsamer Stil* (literally 'sentimental' or 'sensitive style'). J.S. Bach's second son, Carl Philip Emanuel, employed for almost thirty years at the Prussian court of Frederick the Great, became the chief proponent of this style, directly influencing Haydn, Mozart and Beethoven.

Pianos

The notion of applying a keyboard action to an instrument normally played with hammers or mallets is recorded as early as the fifteenth century. The actions of these early struck instruments could be likened, mechanically speaking, to the ancient levered catapult. The 'missile' was a hinged or pivoted hammer which, propelled by the arrested momentum of the keylever, was thrown against a string or bell or metal bar. Analogies aside, the geometry was the critical factor: the keylever had to reach the end of its

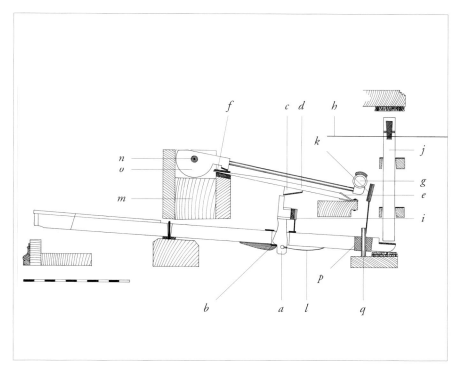

Fig. 4 *Cristofori's piano action. Section at note c''. The drawing represents the fully developed action as found in Cristofori's three surviving pianos, incorporating his two great innovations, the escapement and the check.*

The action operates as follows: The keylever carries an escapement lever (a) in the form of a latch-like component pivoted in a mortise on a leathered ledge (b). In rising it lifts a small leathered block (c) attached to an intermediate lever (d) hinged with leather (e). The leather tip (f) at the opposite end lifts the hammer near its fulcrum, thus accelerating the hammer head (g), a leather-covered paper cylinder, towards the string (h). The simple geometry of the keylever and intermediate lever rising in opposing arcs, ensures that at a certain point they disengage. A leather stop on a flexible wire (i) adjusts this disengagement so that it happens when the hammer is very close to the string, but not in contact with it. In rising, the key lever also lifts a damper (j) from the string and moves a check-pad (k) on a wire stem in an arc towards the hammer head. The check captures the hammer head as long as the key is held down and prevents repercussions of the hammer in forceful playing. When the keylever returns fully to rest, the escapement lever re-latches under the intermediate lever assisted by a spring (l). There is no hammer rest, as such. The hammers are mounted in the slots of a comb-like construction (m) and share a common axle wire (n) passing through a semi-circular butt (o). Cristofori's key guiding system is unconventional: the sides of the distal ends of his keylevers are leathered (p) and guided between wooden dowels (q). Cristofori made no provision for lifting all the dampers simultaneously.

downward travel before the hammer reached the string, so that the hammer, continuing its upward trajectory independently, could strike the string unfettered and then fall away (or recoil) (see Fig.5).

Then in the 1690s, Bartolomeo Cristofori, a Paduan employed at the Medici court in Florence, began to produce a far more sophisticated hammer action stringed keyboard instrument. Highly evolved in both structure and action, and differing from a harpsichord in every essential, except outward appearance, it was named as his contemporaries would undoubtedly have regarded it: *cembalo col piano e forte* or 'harpsichord with soft and loud'. His fully developed action (see Fig.4), as known from his three surviving instruments of the 1720s, involved two crucial and ingenious inventions: i) the adaptation of an escapement to allow the player's finger to remain in contact with the flight of the hammer until it was very close to the string, giving greater dynamic control without the danger of interfering with the free recoil, and ii) the check, which captured and held the recoiling hammer as long as the key was depressed, preventing the hammer from bouncing and striking again. Although his pianos aroused the immediate interest and admiration of the *cognoscenti* at court, it was probably the lack of a challenging and specific repertoire for the new instrument that accounted for the uneven pace of its assimilation into musical life at large. For over a century instrument makers across Europe experimented and struggled, apparently to reinvent or rediscover much of Cristofori's work, in response to a more slowly shifting aesthetic.

However slow, the shift was inexorable. As the eighteenth century progressed, harpsichords, even those fitted with MACHINE STOPS and VENETIAN SWELLS, which ostensibly enabled them to perform the newest music, began to be regarded as old-fashioned. Moreover, advancing technology could now facilitate the production of the sophisticated piano action that Cristofori had anticipated. In short, the piano's moment had arrived. Demand for the 'new' keyboard instrument with its strings struck by recoiling hammers, offering touch-sensitive dynamics and greater volume than a clavichord, would soon overtake that for the plucked keyboards. Although the clavichord had, by this time, fallen out of fashion in most of Europe, in Germany, where it remained popular, piano-inspired registers were introduced.

Playing the early piano repertoire on the type of instrument for which it was conceived can be revelatory, making sense of tempo, pedal and dynamic markings which are difficult or impossible to observe on the modern instrument. The sound and touch of the earliest pianos were softer and lighter than those of the contemporary harpsichords. Although the size and volume of pianos increased steadily, those with Viennese actions, which would have been most familiar to audiences of Mozart, Haydn and Beethoven, possessed a delicacy of touch and transparency of tone which is simply outside the vernacular of the modern piano. In contrast, English pianos were known as the louder instruments, less well damped and thicker textured. Nevertheless, modern ears do not find them loud, and modern piano-trained fingers find them almost uncontrollably light.

Fig. 5 *English square piano action without escapement, after Zumpe c.1767. Section at note c". The hammer shanks (a) carry small leather-covered heads (b) and are hinged with leather to a rail (c) spanning the action. A thin guide wire (d) in a slot in the shank guides the travel. When the key rises, a lifter (e), a leather-covered button on a wire stem, sometimes called the 'old man's head', strikes the underside of the hammer shank near its fulcrum, propelling the hammer head towards the string (f). The front end of the key is arrested by a cloth or leather pad (g) before the hammer has reached the string, so that the hammer, continuing its upward trajectory independently, can strike the string unfettered and recoil without 'blocking' the vibrations it has initiated. As the keylever has risen, it has also lifted a damper lever (h) via a thin strip of whalebone (i). The damper lever is hinged with parchment (j) and has a return spring (k) also of whalebone. Under all the dampers is a leathered batten (l), operated by a hand stop, which rises on inclined planes and lifts all the dampers from the strings. On some pianos of this type, the mechanism is divided to allow treble and bass dampers to be lifted separately.*

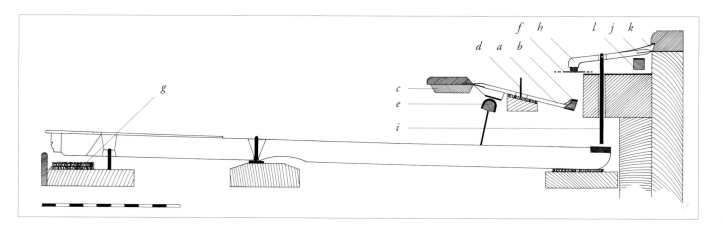

By the end of the eighteenth century in England, pianoforte manufacture was well established among erstwhile harpsichord makers, such as Kirckman and Broadwood. Their former apprentices and workmen, including a significant number of German immigrants, set up new workshops in London, not only to meet the unprecedented demand, but also to develop further and refine the piano action.

Square pianos, actually rectangular in shape, were produced in great numbers to satisfy popular demand for the new instrument. The action in the early squares (see Fig.5) ignored the expensive and elaborate actions derived from Cristofori's invention and reverted to the simpler catapult/arrested-key action described above. Executed with fine craftsmanship and design, it possessed the virtues of superior speed and control of repetition, plus ease of maintenance. Always cheaper, more compact and, in the early years, more readily obtainable than grand pianos, squares existed side by side with them for over a century, attaining a musical significance probably surpassing the modern upright to which they are often likened. The earliest surviving Broadwood square (no.12), dated 1774, by kind bequest of David Wainwright, forms part of the collection at Fenton House. Later squares progressively incorporated the essential elements of Cristofori's action: the escapement, patented by John Geib in London in

Fig. 6 *English grand piano action (with escapement), drawn from a Broadwood grand of 1799. Section at note c".*
Pivoted in the keylever is the hopper (a) which rises when a note is played. The top end of the hopper engages a leathered notch (b) in the hammer butt (c), which is mounted on an axle and carries the hammer shank (d) and hammer head (e). The butt is a complex construction containing an adjustment screw (f) to regulate the friction on the axle. As the force of the hopper is applied close to the hammer's fulcrum, it is accelerated to a velocity much greater than the player's finger. The hopper has an inclined plane (g) which contacts an adjustable leathered set-off stop (h). This has the effect of forcing the tip of the hopper out of the notch in the butt, so that the last part of the hammer's flight is disconnected from the key-impulse. Thus the hammer is free to strike and then recoil so that the strings' vibrations are not inhibited. This disengagement of the hammer, the 'escapement', is precisely adjusted to take place, according to Broadwood's own instructions, when the hammer is 'half of a quarter of an inch from the string'. As the keylever has risen, another component has come into play: the check (i), a leathered pad mounted on a thin iron rod, which because the movement of the keylever is in an arc, is now closer to the falling hammer and captures it. This prevents repercussions of the hammer in forceful playing. When the key returns fully to rest, the check releases the hammer and it falls onto the hammer rest-rail (j) and the hopper re-latches into the notch assisted by a spring (k). The butt has an extra layer of leather or cloth (l) below the notch to ensure this return is silent. As well as raising the hopper and check, the keylever also lifts a damper (m) from the strings. The damper resembles a thin harpsichord jack in dimensions and is guided by similar upper and lower registers (n). The damping material is three layers of thin woollen cloth (o). A notch or dogleg is cut in the stem of the damper so that all the dampers can be raised simultaneously by a hinged rail (p) spanning the instrument and connected to the sustaining pedal.

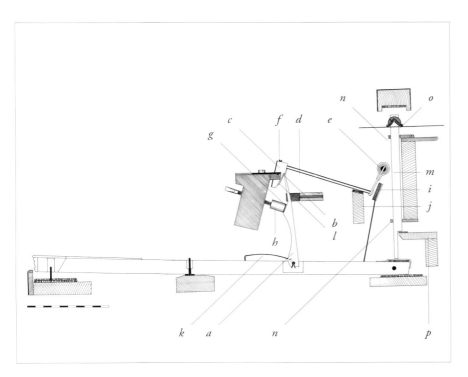

1786, and the check, patented by James Shudi Broadwood in 1825.

Cristofori's direct imitators were few, but his successors in other national traditions reproduced his concepts in a variety of new mechanisms. One of the most important and influential of these was devised by Americus Backers. A Dutch immigrant working in Jermyn Street in London from 1763 to 1779, he developed and perfected the so-called 'English' action for grand pianos, which was copied by Broadwood and others (see Fig.6). Such pianos, not unnaturally, experienced unrivalled popularity in England and were made and survive in great numbers. The solo works of numerous composers, among them Clementi, Dussek and John Field, are closely associated with these instruments. In addition, many of the best-known players and composers across Europe appreciated the qualities of the English piano, both square and grand, and the export market was very healthy. Haydn's last piano sonatas, known as the English sonatas, were composed with these instruments in mind. In December 1817 the Broadwood firm sent a present of a six-octave grand piano to Beethoven, who ordinarily used Viennese-action instruments. Delighted with the gift, he reputedly[9], and quite rightly, would not let it be regulated by anyone unfamiliar with the intricacies of the English action. Beethoven's last three piano sonatas (Opp.109, 110 and 111) have come to be particularly associated with this piano, which later belonged to Liszt.

Eighteenth-Century English and French Harpsichords Contrasted

Late eighteenth-century English harpsichords make up a third of the instruments in the Benton Fletcher Collection. A comparison of their features with those of their possibly more familiar French counterparts (which do not form part of this collection) is offered here in order to clarify certain aspects of each and to help explain their differences.

A common Flemish inheritance informed both English and French harpsichord making throughout the eighteenth century[10]. Nevertheless, different elements of the Flemish style were selected, absorbed and developed in the two countries, blending freely with established indigenous practices. The harpsichords resulting from these parallel processes in France and England were so distinct from each other, and so consistent within their frontiers, as to comprise true national types. When juxtaposed, late eighteenth-century English and French harpsichords reflect substantially different aesthetic ideals, spawned by the essentially divergent social conditions in the two countries. Not unnaturally, the instruments manifest their respective 'tastes' in external appearance, in the internal case and action construction and in the setting up of the action.

The casework of English harpsichords was made primarily from native oak, veneered with handsome panels of figured or exotic woods, such as walnut, mahogany or burr-elm, framed in crossbanding. Occasionally, the keywell depicted musical motifs or trophies in intricate marquetry. Under normal circumstances, soundboards were not decorated. In France and the Low Countries, instead of oak a less dense wood, poplar, was generally used for cases, and then painted, lacquered or elaborately adorned with chinoiserie. Soundboards were decorated (as on the Ruckers harpsichord, no.2) with colourful fruit and flowers, elegant blue borders and arabesques.

The action of double-manual French instruments (see Fig.7) was designed to contrast the timbres of two sets of strings sounding at normal pitch (8' pitch), to combine or 'couple' these by means of a movable upper keyboard, and to allow the addition of a third set of strings sounding an octave higher (4' pitch). The French repertoire of the period, with its highly ornamented character pieces and *style brisé*[11] was also perfectly served by the lightly balanced keyboards and the instruments' rich bass sonorities. English double-manual harpsichords possessed the same three sets of strings, but, being designed to serve the large repertoire of musical transition from the harpsichord to the piano, were set up to facilitate not only more, but also more easily discernible contrasts in timbre and dynamics. This aesthetic aim was realised through the DOGLEG COUPLER, which did not require a movable keyboard, by pedal-operated machine stops and swell mechanisms (devices which created crescendo and diminuendo like the Venetian swell and NAG'S HEAD SWELL) and by the inclusion of a fourth register, the LUTE REGISTER, which, plucking very close to the nut, produced a distinctive nasal sound. The timbres of the two 8's which could be contrasted in English double manual harpsichords, the lute and the back 8', were far more distinct from each other than the timbres of the two 8's on French doubles. This is because the plucking points of these two 8's in English harpsichords were much further apart than the 8's on French harpsichords (see section drawings, Figs 7 and 8). Crucially, on English instruments the pedal-controlled devices allowed players to change the registration and dynamics without taking their hands from the keyboard. Often, even single-manual instruments, such as the 1761 Shudi (no.3) and the 1783 Longman & Broderip (no.17) harpsichords, included machine stops and were set up to allow the largest

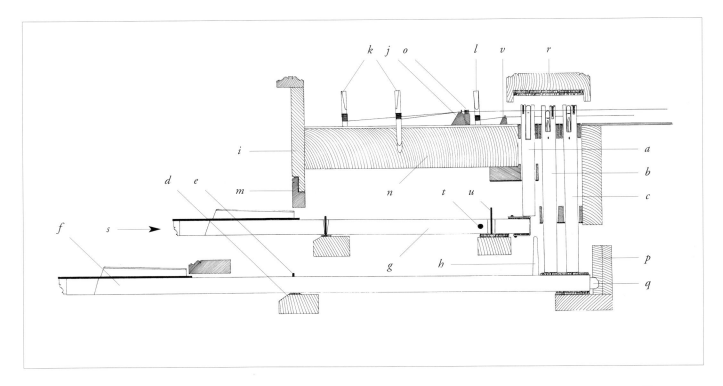

Fig. 7 *Section through the action of a late eighteenth-century double-manual French harpsichord. Note the distance between the plucking points of the two 8's and compare with the lute and back 8' registers on the English action, Fig.8.*

a   *jack, front 8' register*
b   *jack, 4' register*
c   *jack, back 8' register*
d   *balance rail*
e   *balance pin*
f   *lower manual key*
g   *upper manual key*
h   *coupler dog*
i   *nameboard or facia*
j   *8' nut*
k   *8' tuning pins*
l   *4' tuning pins*
m   *name batten*
n   *wrestplank*
o   *buff stop*
p   *rack (rear key guide)*
q   *rear guide*
r   *jackrail*
s   *direction in which upper manual moves to engage coupler dog (h)*
t   *lead key weight*
u   *upper manual rear guide pin*
v   *4' nut*

possible contrast in DYNAMICS and timbre within their limitations[12].

These harpsichords were produced during a relatively settled period in England, characterised by a degree of religious tolerance and social mobility, and rapid industrial growth and expansion. The instruments' capability for sheer volume, clear contrasts and large gestures reflects the demands of a developing middle- and upper-middle-class audience, as much as those of the more traditional patrons of the arts. They were used not only in the royal households, but also in churches, theatres and homes, grand and less grand. Furthermore, late eighteenth-century English harpsichords were expected to serve a repertoire as cosmopolitan as London itself: from Scarlatti, Bach, Bach's sons and Handel, to Rameau and Haydn.

Late eighteenth-century French harpsichords, on the other hand, were the products of a more stratified society and used largely by an exclusive, and quite insular, aristocratic class. With their sometimes extravagant decoration and close association with the music of courtly entertainment, flattery and intrigue, the instruments became potent symbols of the excesses of the ruling elite. As such, many met a fate similar to that of their patrician owners and tragically were destroyed during the Revolution and post-Revolutionary era[13].

Because so few French harpsichords survived these upheavals, and because of their lavish decoration, they have come to be particularly valued, probably

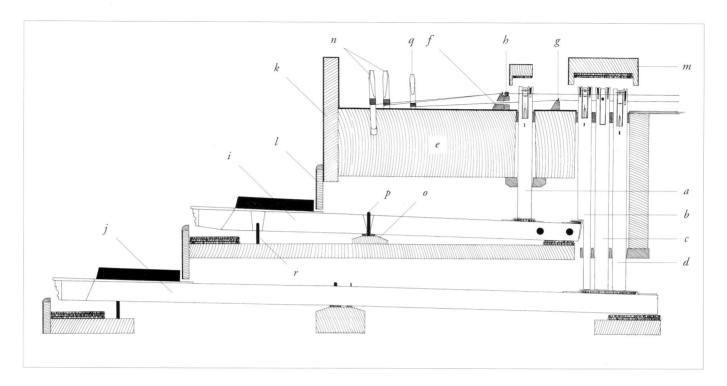

out of proportion to their actual musical influence. Conversely, the fact that late eighteenth-century English harpsichords survive in relatively large numbers has tended to devalue them in modern eyes. Yet they were in such great demand during their own time that they were built on a scale approaching mass production, and they were known and used by court musicians and composers across Europe. In a probable inversion of the historical reality, barely a handful of English harpsichords, the most versatile and widely disseminated keyboard instruments of their time, have been reproduced today. Instead, the instrument most copied and consequently most familiar, not only to modern early music audiences, but also to modern players, is a French Parisian harpsichord of 1770[14]. If English harpsichords now require a measure of advocacy, an important function served by this collection is that it invites modern audiences and aspiring and professional players to become acquainted with the touch and sound-ideal of these magnificent instruments. In short, it stimulates exploration of a voice from the late eighteenth-century musical mainstream.

Fig. 8 Section through the action of a late eighteenth-century double-manual English harpsichord (Shudi & Broadwood 1770, no.1). Compare the distance between the plucking points of the lute register and the back 8' with the distance between the two 8's on the French harpsichord, Fig.7.

a jack, lute register
b jack, front 8' (dogleg) sounds on either the upper or lower manual
c jack, back 8' register
d jack, 4' register
e wrestplank
f 8' nut
g 4' nut
h buff stop
i upper manual key lever
j lower manual key lever
k nameboard or facia
l name batten
m jackrail
n 8' tuning pins
o balance rail
p balance pin
q 4' tuning pin
r touch pin

Preserving A Working Collection

Early keyboard instruments are comparatively lightly built structures. Unlike modern grand pianos, they have no metal frames. Nevertheless, when kept at playing pitch they must withstand a considerable tension exerted by their strings. This can approach a ton in large harpsichords such as the 1770 Shudi & Broadwood harpsichord (no.1) or in a medium-sized early piano such as the 1805 Broadwood (no.14). Even small virginals and clavichords are resisting tensions near to the limit of what their correspondingly light structures can bear. All of these instruments are, therefore, peculiarly vulnerable to damage from the effects of adverse or unstable environmental conditions.

In recognition of the demands of this special type of collection, the National Trust is committed to an ongoing programme of measures aimed at stabilising and improving the environment within Fenton House, which must itself be protected and preserved. Each instrument in the collection is regularly monitored for structural changes, kept in tune, and routinely maintained. Detailed written records are kept of observations and any action taken. As would be expected, all prospective players are individually auditioned and introduced to the instruments before they are permitted to play.

The National Trust realises that interest in early music has now grown far beyond that which Benton Fletcher could possibly have imagined. His appeal for mere recognition of the collection was seemingly solitary; today, in contrast, access to the instruments must be regulated for the sake of their preservation. It is argued, with certain justification, that the playing of original instruments is philosophically unsound. The fidelity of the resemblance of a working antique to the object when new can never be better than conjectural. Furthermore, the continued use of the instrument degrades whatever may remain of its originality. Nevertheless, the conditions of the Benton Fletcher bequest are clear regarding the intention that the instruments be used and regularly maintained. The National Trust feels that here, as in many other buildings and collections, a balance can be struck which satisfies both the duty to preserve our heritage and the need to make it accessible. The excellent condition of the instruments today, and the many educational and pleasurable purposes that the collection fulfils, are witness to the successful and continuing pursuit of this ideal.

1   From a letter in Benton Fletcher's own hand, held in National Trust archives and dated 12 November 1931. He states: 'I write as having been a friend of the founders of your Trust. Miss Octavia Hill, Miss Yorke, and Sir Robert Hunter were all well known to me

personally and I was by them appointed secretary to the Surrey Branch of the Commons Preservation Society...' Octavia Hill, Robert Hunter and Hardwicke Rawnsley are generally considered to be the three founders of the National Trust. Harriot Yorke was a close friend of Miss Hill and also very actively involved in the formation of the Trust. Octavia Hill had suggested that the organisation be called 'The Commons and Gardens Trust', hence Benton Fletcher's reference to the 'Commons Preservation Society'.

2   A transcript of the text is given in Appendix III.

3   I am greatly indebted to Derek Jackson for having allowed me access to all of his mother's papers.

4   The move from Chelsea to Hampstead is described in an article by Roy Willis from a local newspaper, probably the (now defunct) West London Press, dated Friday 25 July 1952, in which Mrs Jackson is interviewed and her contribution acknowledged. I am indebted to Derek Jackson for bringing this article to my attention.

5   Surviving sixteenth-century keyboard instruments made in Britain are exceedingly rare: among these are a claviorganum (a harpsichord and organ combined, actually made by a Flemish maker working in England) and two virginals. There are a greater number of surviving English instruments from the seventeenth century, including 20 English virginals, fewer than five harpsichords and a number of spinets from the later part of the century.

6   Very occasionally, harpsichords included a fourth set of strings at 16' pitch or, more rarely, at 2' pitch.

7   The keyboard works of Domenico Scarlatti, who had unbroken access to early pianos as well as harpsichords throughout his tenure (1746–57) at the Spanish court of Queen Maria Barbara, provide a possible exception. See Kirkpatrick, 1953, pp. 183–5.

8   In a narrow sense, the harpsichord may be regarded as a lute, harp or guitar with a keyboard applied to it; the organ, as a wind instrument with a keyboard applied; and the piano, as a pantaleon or dulcimer with a keyboard applied.

9   Forbes, ed., 1970, p.695.

10 Although by the eighteenth century the Flemish influence was predominant, it should be noted that the complete ancestry of neither tradition is absolutely clear-cut. English and French harpsichord making of the seventeenth and eighteenth centuries also display other traits, notably Italian, but also original or indigenous ones.

11 Literally 'broken style'. Also known as *style luté*. A style of composition, in imitation of the lute, greatly favoured in France but copied everywhere; often with strumming figuration and arpeggios (broken chords), and which exploits the mid to low registers of the harpsichord.

12 French instruments occasionally included knee levers for changing stops, but they were considered exceptional and never achieved the popularity and prevalence that the machine stop did on English harpsichords.

13 Somehow even more lamentable, a large number of confiscated harpsichords intended to be kept for study at the Paris Conservatoire were burned to heat classrooms during subsequent winters. Russell (2/1973, pp.152–4) lists 62 harpsichords confiscated from the nobility during the French Revolution. See also Hubbard, 1965, pp.115–16, and Hess, 1953, p.83, for details of these instruments' destruction.

14 A harpsichord by the Parisian maker, Pascal Taskin. This instrument has the same date as the Shudi & Broadwood (no.1), which, to the knowledge of this writer, has never been faithfully copied in modern times.

Overleaf: Detail of the painting inside the lid of the Italian harpsichord (no.15), depicting a biblical scene.

THE INSTRUMENTS

1 Harpsichord

Burkat Shudi and John Broadwood, London, 1770

One of the largest and most elaborate harpsichords ever made in England. Note the compass, extended by half an octave in the bass to CC. (See also back cover.)

Burkat Shudi, the Swiss cabinet maker and joiner destined to found the business which grew into the famous Broadwood piano firm, left Schwanden, his birthplace, in 1718 at the age of sixteen, to seek work in London. Already trained in cabinet making, he found a position in Hermann Tabel's workshop in Swallow Street, near Piccadilly. Tabel, having learned his craft from descendants of the celebrated Ruckers family of Antwerp (see no.2), is generally credited with conveying those traditions to England through his training of Shudi and Jacob Kirckman, the two rivals whose workshops were to dominate English harpsichord making for two-thirds of the eighteenth century.

It is doubtful whether there was any overlap in the periods that Shudi and the younger Alsatian immigrant spent at Tabel's. If there was, it was only fleeting, for by 1729, the date of Shudi's earliest surviving instrument, he had established his own workshop less than half a mile away in Meard Street, Soho. At about the same time, he married Catherine Wild, the daughter of another Swiss émigré who was a prosperous merchant. After the death of Catherine's father in 1741, the Shudi family, as depicted in the painting now at London's National Portrait Gallery[1], moved to occupy the Wild family's premises in Great Pulteney Street, Golden Square, where a workshop was established.

In 1761, twelve years before Shudi's death, a Scottish cabinet maker named John Broadwood was taken on. At the age of 29, he was older than the usual apprentice and undoubtedly already highly skilled. Gradually, over the next decade, Broadwood became absolutely indispensable to the family business. Within four years, he had become one of Shudi's most trusted craftsmen, working on the instruments that the firm supplied to Frederick the Great of Prussia. Within the next four, he was made a partner after marrying Shudi's daughter, Barbara, in 1769. From then on, both Shudi's and Broadwood's names appeared on harpsichord nameboards until the establishment turned exclusively to piano making during the 1790s. The firm of Broadwood earned the Royal Appointment in the nineteenth century and existed late into the twentieth century before being subsumed by Kemble, a subsidiary of the giant Japanese company, Yamaha.

This harpsichord, completed in 1770, is the earliest surviving with both partners' names on the nameboard, and both names also appear handwritten on the underside of the soundboard, with the date 1769. Designed to serve the complex artistic needs of the period of musical transition from the harpsichord to the piano, it was the largest and most elaborate model of harpsichord ever made in England. It was also the one that seems to have most influenced music in continental European courts. Of the dozen examples that survive, two belonged to Emperor Frederick the Great of Prussia and one to the Empress Maria Theresa of Austria. Perhaps the most famous example in which John Broadwood had a hand, and which survived in Wroclaw (Breslau) until the Second World War, was the one despatched to the Prussian court after having been played by the young Mozart on his visit to London in 1765.

Like the Fenton House harpsichord, all these instruments have (or had) two keyboards with a compass extended by half an octave in the bass. Intriguingly, no music of the period calls for these five notes below FF. In addition to the usual hand stops, they also possess pedal operated devices designed specifically to serve the late eighteenth-century repertoire of musical transition from the harpsichord to the piano. Among these is the VENETIAN SWELL, a mechanism patented by Shudi in the year of this instrument's manufacture (1769). It consists of an inner lid with eleven louvred panels or shutters, which, as they open and close, create crescendo and diminuendo (compare with NAG'S HEAD SWELL on no.6). The whole apparatus can be raised with the outer lid when not required. The pedal operated MACHINE STOP (left pedal) on this and on two of the other double-manual harpsichords in this collection (1762 Kirckman no.9, and 1777 Kirckman no.6) makes four registrations available to the player at the touch of a pedal (see technical data). The BUFF or HARP STOP, which produces a softer, muffled sound, was once operated exclusively by hand stop, but is now controlled by the middle pedal. With its figured veneer panels, decorative lines and crossbanding, and its distinctively shaped and graduated brass lid hinges, the external appearance of this instrument is typical of late eighteenth-century English harpsichords. Unusually the SPINE, which ordinarily was left plain, has been veneered, indicating that it was intended to occupy a position in the centre of a room rather than against a wall. Also atypically, the lid (interior and exterior) and stand have been veneered.

This harpsichord is said to have been made for one Dr Hartley, a friend of Samuel Taylor Coleridge, after whom the poet named his son. By 1885, when it was shown at the International Inventions Exhibition[2], it belonged to William Dale, who wrote a 'Brief Description'[3] of all the keyboard instruments shown in the Loan Collection at the exhibition. In 1913 he published a book entitled *Tschudi the Harpsichord Maker*, which includes a photograph of this harpsichord before the addition of the middle pedal. The instrument was owned by Gerald Cooper before Benton Fletcher acquired it at auction in 1936[4].

◉ CD tracks 1–3

1 According to Boalch, 3/1995, p.174, painted by Marcus Tuscher, a German known to have been working in London *c*.1742.
2 Two other harpsichords now at Fenton House were also, coincidentally, shown at this exhibition: the 1612 Ruckers (no.2) and the 1752 Kirckman (no.16).
3 I am indebted to Andrew Garrett for calling to my attention the existence of this guide to the International Inventions Exhibition (Dale, 1885). See also Hipkins, 1885.
4 According to Boalch 3/1995, p.620, sold at Puttick and Simpson's on 20 February 1936.

Makers Burkat Shudi and John Broadwood

Date and place 1770, London

Nameboard inscription
Burkat Shudi et Johannes Broadwood
No.625 Londini Fecerunt 1770

Other inscriptions
i   On the underside of the soundboard:
    Burkat Shudi et Joh. Broadwood Londini
    facit [sic] 1769.
ii On the wrestplank against the treble 8'
    nut: Restored by Charles Hersant, 49
    Lennox Road, Stroud Green Road N
    London.
iii On the back of the name batten:
    Repaired by Henry John Dale,
    Cheltenham 1882.
iv On the back of the name batten: Arnold
    Dolmetsch Ltd., Haslemere 1951, C.
    Leslie C. Ward [signed].

Case materials and dimensions
Oak, veneered with panels of burr walnut,
crossbanded with mahogany, lines in
boxwood and ebony in a repeating pattern of
long dashes and short crosses. Lid, interior
and exterior, spine and stand also veneered.
Length 2674, width 1011, depth 321.

Compass	CC–f''', chromatic
3-octave span	486 (lower keyboard)
	485 (upper keyboard)

Disposition	Two keyboards
←4'	lower keyboard
8'→	(leather plectra) lower keyboard
←8' dogleg	lower and upper keyboards
←8' lute	upper keyboard
buff to 8'→	lower keyboard

Six hand stops with turned brass knobs,
controlling the above registers (handstop to
the buff stop is now disconnected) and the
machine stop; three pedals operating, from left
to right: the machine stop, the buff stop and
the Venetian swell. When the machine stop is
engaged and the pedal is up, the lower manual
sounds all three sets of strings and the upper
sounds the front 8'. With the pedal depressed,
the lower manual sounds the back 8' (leather
plectra) and the upper, the lute stop.

Stringing and scaling
Two sets of 8' strings and one 4'

	←8'			8'→		4'	
	string length	dogleg pluck point	lute pluck point	string length	pluck point	string length	pluck point
f'''	132	50	13	126	66	60	46
c'''	172	61	16	164	76	81	52
f''	257	73	21	245	89	122	58
c''	364	83	22	322	98	163	63
f'	522	95	29	497	110	244	67
c'	695	107	33	665	122	327	72
f	981	120	39	946	134	478	78
c	1193	131	43	1158	142	599	84
F	1468	146	50	1437	162	772	92
C	1668	157	57	1637	173	896	98
FF	1941	174	62	1912	190	1073	105
CC	2067	184	67	2054	201	1198	111

String gauge numbers are stamped on the nuts. On the 8' nut the numbers are centred
between the pairs of strings for the indicated note. On the 4' nut the majority of the
numbers are positioned closer to the lower note of each pair.

8'		4'	
between the pair of strings for	gauge no.	between	gauge no.
c''	4	b and c'	4
b	5	eb and e	5
e	6	A and Bb	6
Bb	7	F and F#	7
F#	8	C# and D	8
D	9	AA and BBb	9
BB	10	FF# and GG	10
AA	11	EE and FF	11
GG	12	CC# and DD	12
FF	13	CC and CC#	13
DD	14		
CC	15		

Present pitch a' = 415.3 Hz

2 Harpsichord

Ioannes Ruckers, Antwerp, 1612
enlarged in England, 18th century

Although not strictly part of the Benton Fletcher Collection, this harpsichord has been displayed alongside it for many years: first in Chelsea at the house acquired by Major Fletcher and the National Trust after the original home for the collection, Old Devonshire House, was destroyed in the Second World War. The instrument was then moved with the collection to Fenton House in 1952. Belonging to Her Majesty Queen Elizabeth II, it was previously displayed at Windsor Castle from at least Queen Victoria's time, and still bears, on its bottom boards, a stamped Windsor accession number. By 1883, even before it was shown at the International Inventions Exhibition of 1885, it had acquired its present new set of ivory key coverings. It is unclear whether the replacement was occasioned by the removal by visitors of many of the old ones for souvenirs when it was on display at Windsor, or whether, even then, it had new coverings.

Keywell showing the full inscription. The decorative papers in the key- and stringwells date from the 1981 restoration and are copies of patterns from surviving fragments actually found on this instrument.

Opposite: Reputed to have been owned by Handel, the harpsichord was enlarged in England in the eighteenth century. At this time it also acquired its black lacquered exterior and vermilion lid interior.

A cautious association with the 'large harpsichord' mentioned in Handel's will appears in A.J. Hipkins's exhibition catalogue of 1885[1]. By 1892, when it was sent for exhibition in the Internationale Ausstellung für Musik und Theaterwesen in Vienna, the suggestion of the link with Handel seems to have solidified, without real basis, into a statement of fact. Modern research has failed to establish an unambiguous documentary link[2], yet the composer's name continues to be associated with this Ruckers harpsichord. While it is unlikely that Handel ever owned it, his partiality to instruments by that

The authentic H(ans) R(uckers) rose, photographed from the keyboard end.

renowned sixteenth- and seventeenth-century family of keyboard instrument makers is well established.

Almost no Ruckers harpsichords survive in a structural or musical condition unaltered since manufacture. Eighteenth-century instrument makers routinely changed and enlarged these desirable Flemish instruments, in a process called RAVALEMENT, to suit contemporary musical requirements. Whatever else may have been altered or replaced, the Ruckers name was scrupulously preserved during these metamorphoses, for, as a recognised badge of quality, it always commanded a premium. It is therefore not surprising that the name was often deceitfully applied to later instruments, whether or not they possessed any remnant of Ruckers workmanship.

An unknown English maker enlarged this instrument during the eighteenth century[3]. Very fortunately, the original Ruckers SOUNDBOARD, with its authentic HR (Hans Ruckers) ROSE and characteristic fruit and floral decoration with blue scalloped borders and arabesques, survives intact. The scope of the ravalement can be discerned at the treble end of the BENTSIDE just before the curve tightens, where the join between the original Ruckers case and the eighteenth-century English extension is visible.

◎ CD tracks 4–5

1 Hipkins, 1885. A.J. Hipkins, a leading member and director of the Broadwood firm during the late nineteenth century, may have been the first to have made this tentative association in a letter to the Athenaeum of September 1883, a typed copy of which is in National Trust Archives (Hughenden Manor) on a page numbered 1327. Coincidentally, the 1752 Kirckman harpsichord (no.16) and the Shudi & Broadwood harpsichord (no.1) were also shown at this exhibition and appear in Hipkins's catalogue.
2 MacTaggart and MacTaggart, 1983, pp.92–3.
3 The original Ruckers disposition of this harpsichord is described in detail by O'Brien, 1990, p.243.

Makers Ioannes Ruckers and unknown 18th-century English maker

Date and place 1612, Antwerp and 18th century, England

Nameboard inscription
Ioannes Ruckers me fecit Antverpiæ 1612

Other inscriptions
i   On the back of the name batten: C.L.C.W [Leslie Ward, of Dolmetsch], 1970.
ii On the back of the name batten: Restored by Henry Tull, 3 Leopold Road, Ealing Common, London. Sept. 29th 1938.
iii On the back of the name batten: Restored by Douglas Campbell-Brown, Ewell June, 1951.
iv On the back of the name batten: J. [or possibly I].
v   On the back of the name batten: Ioannes Ruckers me fecit Antverpiæ 1612.
vi On the bottom boards: V[ictoria] R[egina], 866, Windsor Castle, Room 528 [stamped, including the royal insignia].

Case materials and dimensions
Original exterior parts, black lacquered poplar. Length 2303, width 879, depth 272.

Compass	*GG–f'''*, no *GG♯*
3-octave span	487 (lower and upper keyboards)
Disposition	Two keyboards.
←4'	lower keyboard
8'→	lower keyboard
←8' dogleg	lower and upper keyboards

Three hand stops with turned ivory knobs, controlling the above registers.

Stringing and scaling
Two sets of 8' strings and one 4'

	←8'		8'→		4'	
	string length	*pluck point*	*string length*	*pluck point*	*string length*	*pluck point*
f'''	132	52	127	67	59	48
c'''	170	59	162	75	77	54
f''	261	72	245	88	116	61
c''	353	82	336	98	151	67
f'	531	92	508	114	248	74
c'	698	108	670	123	329	79
f	954	123	924	140	466	86
c	1162	135	1128	151	585	93
F	1450	152	1421	169	775	100
C	1648	165	1625	181	916	106
GG	1723	175	1714	191	1017	110

String gauge numbers are stamped on the 8' nut. The numbers are centred between the pairs of strings for the indicated note. There is no indication for the lowest strings because the bassmost section of the nut has been replaced.

	8'
between the pair of strings for	*gauge no.*
c''	4
c'	5
b	6
g	6
f♯	7
d	7
c♯	8
B	8
F♯	8
F	9
E♭	9

Present pitch *a' = 415.3 Hz*

3 Harpsichord

Burkat Shudi, London, 1761

Opposite: An excellent example of the standard single manual model late eighteenth-century English harpsichord. The pedal on the post-war stand operates the machine stop, an integral part of the instrument's musical aesthetic.

This instrument had belonged to the pianist Fanny Davies (1861–1934), a pupil of Clara Schumann[1]. During her long career, Miss Davies was especially noted for her fine interpretation of the standard piano repertoire and for her chamber music performances. Less well documented was her keen interest in earlier keyboard music, especially English virginals music, which she performed in concert on period instruments, long before this became fashionable. In 1932, two years before her death, she sold this harpsichord at auction, where it was acquired by Benton Fletcher[2]. During the spring of 1934 he lent it to a large group for a performance of Bach's St Matthew Passion in Westminster Abbey. The concert was reviewed by *The Times* and the comments, singling out the qualities of the harpsichord, were quoted by Benton Fletcher on many subsequent occasions, including a radio broadcast in 1938:

> *I should like to read to you what a music critic wrote after I lent a harpsichord to Westminster Abbey for the St. Matthew Passion by Bach: Here it is: 'From my seat in the nave it was not possible to hear the recitation or the orchestra distinctly, but oddly enough, the harpsichord came through quite clearly.' As there were two hundred performers this speaks well for the instrument, dated 1761.*

View of the keywell, showing the typical keyboard compass (FF-f''', no FF#), the name batten inscription, and the narrow box on the spine housing the machine stop mechanism.

The year of its manufacture, 1761, is also that in which the Scottish cabinet maker, John Broadwood, joined the Shudi firm (see Shudi & Broadwood harpsichord 1770, no.1). The average yearly output of the workshop during the period when this harpsichord was made (1750–69), is reckoned at fifteen, and its cost would have been in the region of 40 guineas[3].

The pedal operated MACHINE STOP on this SINGLE-MANUAL harpsichord almost obviates the need for a second keyboard by making possible an easy, immediate and large contrast in TIMBRE and DYNAMICS (see technical data). The only facility present in the standard DOUBLE-MANUAL model (e.g. the Kirckman harpsichord 1777, no.6) and lacking in this, the typical English single-manual model, was the LUTE REGISTER[4]. Shudi's instruments, unlike those of Kirckman, never had soundboard ROSES.

⊙ CD tracks 27–29

1   A composer and distinguished concert pianist and teacher in her own right, Clara Schumann (*née* Wieck) was also the wife of the composer Robert Schumann.
2   According to Boalch, 1956, 2/1974 and 3/1995, sold at Puttick & Simpson's on 23 June 1932.
3   Boalch, 2/1974, p.157.
4   Although Longman & Broderip made single-manual harpsichords which also included a lute register.

Maker Burkat Shudi

Date and place 1761, London

Nameboard inscription
Burkat Shudi No.423 Fecit Londini 1761

Other inscriptions
i   On the underside of the soundboard:
    No. 427.
ii On the wrestplank against the treble 4'
    nut: Restored by Charles Hersant 49
    Lennox Road London 19[??].
iii On the back of the name batten: B¤S
    No. 423 [stamped].
iv On 4' jack no.1: B¤S No. 423
    [stamped].
v   On the back of the name batten:
    Repaired by Arnold Dolmetsch Ltd.
    Haslemere Surrey 1950 Leslie Ward
    [signed] Leslie Ward [stamped].
vi On a label on the back of the name
    batten: John Barnes, Dec. 1969. Details
    in restoration report.

Case materials and dimensions
Oak, veneered with burr elm panels,
crossbanded with mahogany, lines in maple
or holly. Length 2316, width 931, depth
271.

Compass FF–f''', no FF♯

3-octave span 486

Disposition One keyboard
      ←4'
        8'→
      ←8'
buff to 8'→

Five hand stops with turned brass knobs,
controlling the above registers and the
machine stop. One pedal operating the
machine stop. When the machine stop
knob is engaged and the pedal is up, all
three sets of strings sound; when the
pedal is depressed, the 4' and front 8' are
withdrawn, leaving only the back 8'
sounding.

Stringing and scaling
Two sets of 8' strings and one 4'

	←8'		8'→		4'	
	string length	pluck point	string length	pluck point	string length	pluck point
f'''	134	42	127	57	63	47
c'''	175	53	166	68	83	52
f''	263	67	251	83	122	59
c''	353	79	336	94	164	64
f'	529	93	504	108	249	73
c'	698	102	668	117	330	78
f	984	118	952	134	481	86
c	1196	132	1162	147	601	92
F	1478	148	1449	164	768	101
C	1680	161	1649	179	886	107
FF	1853	175	1834	194	1028	113

String gauge numbers are stamped on the 8' nut for gauges 4 and 5, but handwritten on
replacement nut for the rest. For the 4', no gauges are indicated for the lowest three
notes where the nut has been replaced. There is a handwritten gauge 6, also on
replacement nut. All other 4' gauge numbers have been stamped and are original.

8'		4'	
between the pair of strings for	gauge no.	between	gauge no.
f'	4	c' and c♯'	4
c'	5	f and f♯	5
g	6	B and c	6
d	7	F♯ and G	7
A	8	E♭ and E	8
G	9	BB and C	9
E	9		
E♭	9		
C	10		
AA	11		
GG♯	11		
GG	12		

Present pitch a' = 415.3 Hz

4 Virginals

Marcus Siculus, Sicily, 1540

The oldest signed and dated instrument in the collection, this is the unique extant example of Marcus Siculus's work. Almost everything about this virginals, from its intricate mouldings to the details of its inner construction, betrays an unusual refinement and attention to detail. The fronts of the boxwood NATURALS retain remnants of the green paper which would have shown through the carved and pierced arcades. The extravagant tracery ROSE is especially fine and remarkably well preserved. Delicately drawn in black in the string- and keywells are symmetrical floral decorations which anticipate the block-printed paper patterns that began to appear later in the century in Flemish harpsichords and virginals (compare with the 1612 Ruckers, no.2)[1]. Punctuating the upper case edge at regular intervals and dotting the black (probably ebony) ACCIDENTALS are ivory or bone

studs: a very characteristic, if relatively restrained, example of the applied decoration common at the time.

Ordinarily, these lightly built Italian virginals rested inside protective wooden cases (see also the single-strung Italian harpsichord, no.15), cheaply made, but lavishly decorated. This instrument would certainly have possessed such a case, for its decoration is confined to the inner surfaces and other areas which would have remained visible when the virginals was placed inside its box.

Earlier catalogues of the collection express suspicion about the authenticity of the inscription, for nothing is known of Siculus's life. Nevertheless, the features of this virginals conform to what is now known of the craft and techniques of instrument making of its time, as well as to

The virginals is the earliest signed and dated instrument in the collection, and the inscription can be seen on the jackrail. Note the symmetrical floral decorations.

contemporary musical expectations. In addition, research has most recently established that, as his name suggests, Siculus probably did live and work in Sicily. The critical measurements of the case and action all translate into convenient multiples or divisions of the sixteenth-century standard unit of measure in Palermo[2].

Although the compass up to *f'''* is a relatively common one for such instruments (cf. no.5), no written music of the period calls for the highest notes[3]. Their inclusion on such early virginals may have served to improve the quality of the more commonly used high notes, or to allow limited octave transposition in imitation of the octavino, a popular 'miniature' instrument, designed to sound at 4' pitch. It is interesting that so high a treble range was complemented by such a relatively modest bass compass, although this was effectively extended by the SHORT OCTAVE. This arrangement, exceedingly common throughout the sixteenth and seventeenth centuries, made the more commonly used diatonic notes (or naturals) available in the bass in place of the rarely needed accidentals, as shown below.

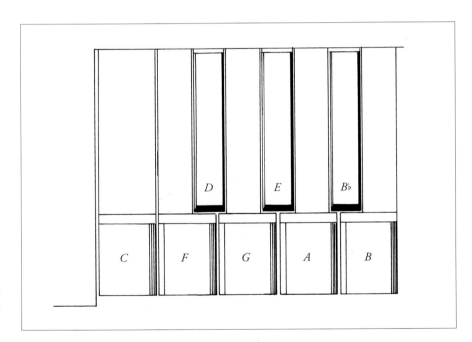

Fig. 9 *The bass notes in instruments like the Siculus have a C/E short octave. The apparent G# sounds E, F# sounds D, and E sounds C. The keys are labelled as they sound.*

○ CD tracks 22–24

1 I am grateful to Grant O'Brien for calling my attention to this similarity.
2 O'Brien, 1999, pp.125–7.
3 Indeed, few seventeenth-century harpsichords reached beyond *c'''* or *d'''*. Remarkably, over more than 250 years, until plucked keyboard instruments died out at the end of the eighteenth century, the treble compass seldom exceeded the *f'''* on this early virginals. The most notable exception is the significant proportion of eighteenth-century spinets which were designed to cover a full five octaves from GG to g''' (e.g. both the English bentside spinets, nos 7 and 8).

Maker Marcus Siculus

Date and place 1540, Palermo, Sicily

Nameboard inscription
none

Other Inscriptions
i On the jackrail: Marcus Siculus faciebat MDXXXX.
ii On the back of the name batten: [just legible] Repaired [Dolmet]sch Haslemere 1957.

Case materials and dimensions
Cypress. Length 1283, maximum width 339 (excluding the projecting key cheeks, 451 including them), depth 178 (including the cap moulding).

Compass   *C/E* short octave – *f'''*

3-octave span   510

Stringing and scaling
One set of 8' strings. The lowest jack faces towards the player.

	string length	pluck point
f'''	107	76
c'''	143	70
f''	211	61
c''	306	85
f'	439	103
c'	595	144
f	803	188
c	969	226
F	1077	189
C/E	1102	188

There are no string gauge numbers.

Present pitch *a'* = 409 Hz

5 Virginals

attributed to Vincentius Pratensis, Italy, late 16th or early 17th century

This pentagonal instrument was formerly ascribed to the Venetian maker Antonio Baffo (fl.1570–81), although the origin of the attribution is unknown. An issue of *Musical Opinion* (March 1936) described an Italian virginals, loaned by Benton Fletcher for exhibit at Eastbury Manor, Barking, which was 'of sixteenth-century date', made by 'Buffa of Venice', with 'boxwood naturals' and a compass 'running from C (no C♯) to D'[1]. The virginals is, indeed, the only instrument in the collection to have this compass, but its key coverings and arcades (arch-shaped key fronts) are of ivory, not boxwood. On the basis of its moulding and arcade profiles and other details of its construction and decoration, it is now thought to be the work of Vincentius Pratensis (that is, Vincentius of Prato, near Florence, fl.1610–12)[2].

Scratched on the soundboard is a partly legible inscription, possibly dating from a restoration: '…bo…dalla spinetta…1791'. Perhaps it was at this time that the treble end of the left-hand BRIDGE was re-sited, shortening

Right: The virginals rests on a twentieth-century stand made by Dolmetsch.

Opposite: SOUNDBOARD showing the ROSE, the partly legible inscription, possibly dating from a restoration, and the lighter crescent of wood indicating the area where the treble end of the left-hand bridge was originally sited. The JACKS are twentieth-century replacements.

the scaling (sounding length of the strings) between g' and b'', and that the present unoriginal keyboard was acquired. It appears that the original BALANCE RAIL was retained in this alteration, because the plugged BALANCE PIN holes of the original compass (which was the same as the Marcus Siculus virginals), *C/E* SHORT OCTAVE to *f'''*, are clearly visible on the balance rail[3]. Fortunately, the original ivory key coverings and arcades (on which the attribution to Vincentius is partly based) were also re-used, as evidenced by the considerable wear on the heads (proximal portion of the key coverings) and the adjustment of the width of the tail (distal portion of the key covering) for the note D.

Although also lightly built, this instrument is more robust in dimension and sound than the delicate Siculus virginals (no.4). It, too, would have possessed a protective and decorative outer wooden box. Each of these two Italian virginals has its own musical strengths, but together they demonstrate the wide variety that existed in nominally similar types.

CD tracks 18–20

1   Anon., 1936.
2   Wraight, 1992, pp. 131–2.
3   An extra plugged balance pin hole at the very top of the compass, between *e'''* and *f'''*, remains enigmatic.

Maker   attributed to Vincentius Pratensis

Date and place   probably late 16th or early 17th century, Prato, Italy

Nameboard inscription
none

Other inscriptions
i   On the soundboard: [indecipherable]bo dalla spinetta [partly decipherable, looks like 'n 3 – 7 Cre'] 1791.

Case materials and dimensions
Softwood and cypress, painted black with thin gold bands and arabesques. Length 1552, width 403 (excluding the projecting key cheeks; 508 including them), depth 223 (including the cap moulding).

Compass   *C–d'''*, no *C♯*

3-octave span   509

Stringing and scaling
One set of 8' strings. The lowest jack faces towards the player.

	string length	pluck point
d'''	125	64
c'''	132	62
f''	190	61
c''	257	71
f'	426	130
c'	540	153
f	808	235
c	985	291
F	1242	316
C	1346	287

String gauge numbers are handwritten in ink on the wrestplank next to the wrestpins for the notes indicated.

at or between the pins for	gauge no.
e''	10
f♯'	9
b and c'	8 [written on its side]
e	7
B♭	6
F♯	5
E♭ and E	4

Present pitch   *a'* = 440 Hz

6 Harpsichord

Jacob and Abraham Kirckman, London, 1777

The origins of the prolific Kirckman firm were in the London workshop of Hermann Tabel (see no.1). Jacob Kirckman was born near Strasbourg in 1710 and died at Greenwich in 1792. Although the exact dates of his apprenticeship to Tabel are unknown, it is certain that he had earned himself the position of foreman by the time of his master's death in 1738. An oft-cited example of

Caricature of a member of the Kirckman family, probably Abraham; pen and ink drawing with wash (c.1785), by John Nixon.

Opposite: The trestle stand, a reproduction of the type made by Kirckman, was made by Adlam Burnett in the late 1970s. The left pedal operates the machine stop and the right, the nag's head swell; the mechanism for the latter is visible on the underside of the lid. For a complete view of the keywell, see p.14.

Kirckman's business acumen is his precipitate marriage, within a month of Tabel's death, to his widow, thereby becoming 'possessed of all [his] seasoned wood, tools, and stock-in-trade'. In mitigation, however, it should be noted that the former Mrs Tabel would have had as much to gain as her astute suitor did by the seamless perpetuation of her late husband's business. By 1772 Jacob

Kirckman, in the absence of offspring from this marriage[1], had taken his nephew, Abraham, into partnership. From 1789, possibly on the retirement of Jacob, Abraham worked with his son, Joseph. Later, his son, also called Joseph, entered the business, by then all but exclusively devoted to piano making. The business amalgamated with Collard & Collard in 1896 and was later taken over by Chappell, now a trading name belonging to Yamaha[2]. It is poignant that the descendants of the rival eighteenth-century firms, Shudi & Broadwood and Kirckman, which sprang from the same source (i.e. the workshop of Hermann Tabel), should be reunited in the twentieth century under the same Japanese parent company.

During the second half of the eighteenth century, those rival houses virtually monopolised the London harpsichord building trade, but the number of surviving Kirckman plucked keyboard instruments (about 170 harpsichords and a very few spinets), exceeds by more than a factor of three that of his competitor. Significantly, using the same measure (number of surviving instruments), Shudi's firm later (under the Broadwood name) overtook Kirckman's in the production of pianos.

Given that the two masters, Kirckman and Shudi, had trained in the same shop, and were producing instruments on a very large scale, it is hardly surprising to find not only copious similarities between their *oeuvres*, but also a certain standardisation of models. This harpsichord embodies all of the features of the typical English DOUBLE-MANUAL model, with its DOGLEG COUPLER, LUTE REGISTER, pedal-operated MACHINE STOP, and LID or NAG'S HEAD SWELL. The last, a cheaper but almost equally effective version of the VENETIAN SWELL (cf. Shudi & Broadwood, no.1), together with the machine stop, allowed players to create the dynamic contrasts required by the new music being written with performance on the piano, as well as the harpsichord, in mind. The gilt ROSE is of Kirckman's late design.

◉ CD track 30

Soundboard rose, photographed from the keyboard end. The rose is of the third design used by Kirckman. See entries nos.16 and 9 respectively for the first and second designs.

1   The new Mrs Kirckman, *née* Susanna Virgoe, died only two years after Tabel, in October 1740.
2   Known in the UK as Yamaha-Kemble Music (UK) Ltd. I am grateful to Mr Nigel Hill, manager of piano sales at Chappell, New Bond Street, London, for kindly providing background information regarding his firm.

Makers Jacob and Abraham Kirckman

Date and place 1777, London

Nameboard inscription

Jacobus et Abraham Kirckman Londini
fecerunt 1777

Other inscriptions

i   On the wrestplank: Leslie Ward
    [stamped].
ii On the back of the name batten:
    Repaired, C.L.C. Ward. Haslemere.
iii On a label on the back of the name
    batten: Reconstructed 1975, Adlam
    Burnett, Historical Keyboard
    Instruments Ltd.

Case materials and dimensions

Oak, veneered with panels of curled
Cuban mahogany, crossbanded with
mahogany, lines in a chevron pattern in
boxwood and ebony. Length 2360, width
936, depth 320.

Compass   *FF-f'''*, no *FF#*

3-octave span   487 (lower keyboard)
                    485 (upper keyboard)

Disposition   Two keyboards
←4'   lower keyboard
8'→   lower keyboard
←8' dogleg   lower and upper
             keyboards
←8' lute   upper keyboard
buff to 8'→ lower keyboard

Six hand stops with turned brass knobs,
controlling the above registers and the
machine stop. Two pedals operating: the
machine stop (left) and the nag's head (or
lid) swell (right). When the machine stop is
engaged and the pedal is up, the lower
manual sounds all three sets of strings and
the upper sounds the front 8'. With the
pedal depressed, the lower manual sounds
the back 8' and the upper, the lute stop.

Stringing and scaling

Two sets of 8' strings and one 4'

	←8'			8'→		4'	
	string length	dogleg pluck point	lute pluck point	string length	pluck point	string length	pluck point
f'''	129	50	17	123	65	60	47
c'''	169	59	18	164	74	84	51
f''	254	71	22	244	86	128	58
c''	342	79	23	327	95	173	62
f'	516	93	27	496	109	261	71
c'	694	104	32	667	120	344	76
f	982	121	38	954	134	483	84
c	1191	132	42	1163	147	599	88
F	1457	152	53	1435	165	768	96
C	1636	165	58	1614	182	887	102
FF	1755	182	67	1746	199	1029	109

String gauge numbers are stamped on the 8' nut between the pairs of strings for the
indicated note. There are no 4' gauge numbers.

8'	
between the pair of strings for	gauge no.
f'''	4
c''	4
b''	5
c'	5
b	6
f#	6
f	7
c#	7
c	8
A	8
F#	8
F	9
D	9
C#	10
BB	10
BB♭	11
AA	11
GG#	12
FF	13

Present pitch   *a' = 415.3 Hz*

7 Spinet

Unsigned, formerly attributed to Thomas Hitchcock,
London, first half of the 18th century

Before the end of the seventeenth century, small wing-shaped bentside spinets had begun to displace the English virginals (see no.11) as the ordinary instrument for domestic use. Samuel Pepys recounts in a diary entry of 4 April 1668 a visit to Aldgate Street to see Charles Hayward 'that makes virginalls': '[I] did there like of a little espinettes and will have him finish them for me; for I had a mind to a small harpsicon, but this takes up less room and will do my business as to finding out of chords – and I am very well pleased that I have found it.' Pepys's instrument was delivered to him in July and cost £5[1].

This later anonymous BENTSIDE spinet with the walnut case and gilded and chased strap hinges was probably made in London during the first half of the eighteenth century, perhaps in 1742 (if the number inscribed on the highest key is actually a date of manufacture). Although spinets possessed only a single set of strings without any mechanisms for varying volume or timbre, they offered, by the time of this instrument, a full five-octave compass to players lacking the space or means for a harpsichord. The central ivory strip in the ebony accidentals of this keyboard is associated with Hitchcock's work, but a reliable attribution cannot be made on the basis of this alone, as other features of the instrument depart from his usually consistent structural and decorative practices.

The presence of additional bracing inside the instrument, and the inscriptions on the facia and WRESTPLANK[2], indicate a chequered history of repair and restoration. Neither the date nor the circumstances in which it lost its original SOUNDBOARD, wrestpins and JACKS are documented, nor are those in which it acquired its internal accretions. Nevertheless, its most recent restoration has given it a set of jacks[3] closely modelled on those by Hitchcock, which, together with the largely original keyboard, may lend it a touch characteristic of the English bentside spinet of its time.

1 Boalch, 2/1974, p.65; and Latham, ed., 1979, p.247. The Hayward in question was Charles, a member of a famous seventeenth-century family of London keyboard instrument makers.
2 Leslie Ward, a leading member of the Dolmetsch firm, stamped his name (as was his usual practice) on the wrestplank and reverse of the nameboard, where the date 1950 and Dolmetsch's Haslemere address is also written in ink. See technical data.
3 New jacks made in 2000 by Miles Hellon, Greenwich, London.

Maker unknown

Date and place probably first half of the 18th century (but see inscription i below), London

Nameboard inscription
none

Other inscriptions
i   On the highest key: 1742.
ii On the wrestplank: Leslie Ward [stamped].
iii On the back of the facia: Leslie Ward [stamped], Dolmetsch, Haslemere, 1950 [written in ink].

Case materials and dimensions
Walnut, with boxwood lines, but with a mahogany lid. Length 1840, maximum width 587 (excluding the key cheeks, which project 131 from the front case side with which they are perpendicular), depth 177.

Compass   GG–g'''

3-octave span   496

Stringing and scaling
One set of 8' strings. The lowest jack faces away from the player.

	string length	pluck point
g'''	85	37
c'''	131	52
g''	179	74
c''	262	87
g'	377	107
c'	554	123
g	735	144
c	983	158
G	1208	179
C	1405	193
GG	1524	185

There are no string gauge numbers.

Present pitch a' = 415.3 Hz

8 Spinet

inscribed John Hancock, London, late 18th century

This English BENTSIDE spinet, a later example than the anonymous one (no.7), probably dates from the second half of the eighteenth century. It, too, has the five-octave compass that served for most solo and all continuo repertoire. Its handsome mahogany exterior now betrays no evidence of Benton Fletcher's avowal that he rescued it from an outhouse in Wales, where he found 'the top was split into a hundred pieces, rain was falling on it, and the wood was warped'[1]. Nevertheless, certain anomalous features of the interior do divulge a history complicated by intervention and neglect.

The name batten and facia showing the dubious inscription, imperfectly Latinised, as well as the two unrelated patterns of lines which appear on the name batten and around the rippled maple panels on the facia.

The inscription on the exterior of the name batten must be regarded as unreliable, because of its poor execution and the evident reworking of the central cartouche. In addition, when such inscriptions were rendered in Latin, the name 'John' normally became 'Johannes', not 'Johann', and 'London' became 'Londini'. The keywell as a whole displays a very uncharacteristic use of different, rather than matching or related, patterns of lines (ornamental banding). The CHEEKS, name batten and key-endblocks have a peculiar, perhaps even unique, pattern, while the more regular stringing on the facia

Maker unknown

Date and place late 18th century, London

Nameboard inscription
Johann Hancock fecit London

Other inscriptions
i   On the back of the name batten:
    Repaired, Alec Hodsdon, Lavenham,
    Suffolk. 1948 [handwritten in ink].
ii On the back of the name batten:
    Restored by C.L.C. Ward F.R.S.A.,
    M.S.I.A of A. Dolmetsch Ltd.,
    Haslemere, 1956. [handwritten in ink].

Case materials and dimensions
Oak, veneered with mahogany panels and
crossbanding, boxwood and ebony lines;
spine and bottom, softwood; mahogany lid.
Length 1987, maximum width 650
(excluding the key cheeks, which project
169 from the front case side with which
they are perpendicular), depth 230.

Compass GG–g'''

3-octave span   487

Stringing and scaling
One set of 8' strings. The lowest jack faces
away from player.

	string length	pluck point
g'''	130	56
c'''	170	63
g''	235	75
c''	331	77
g'	459	90
c'	647	95
g	826	105
c	1041	112
G	1220	122
C	1409	123
GG	1530	138

There are no string gauge numbers.

Present pitch a' = 415.3 Hz

appears on other instruments, including the exterior of the 1770 Shudi & Broadwood harpsichord (no.1). Unfortunately, no other instrument by John Hancock survives with which to compare these features.

The keyboard, possibly adapted from another instrument, may be a late nineteenth- or early twentieth-century replacement, judging from details of construction and the piano-like depth of the key levers[2]. The JACKS, although original, are now loaded with three lead pellets each in order to ensure the return of these heavy levers. When and by whom this work may have been done is undocumented, although there are two twentieth-century signatures on the reverse of the nameboard (see Other inscriptions in the technical data, right).

CD tracks 6–7

1   Nicholson, Hubert, 'A Living Museum of Old Music', The Bazaar, *Exchange and Mart*: Vol. CXXIX, no.37, 14 September 1937, p.1.
2   In either case, a chronology which adequately accounts for the presence of a second set of balance mortises approximately one inch further from the player than those in use at present is difficult to construct. The proximal set of mortises certainly provides superior repetition, but is still not good enough for ordinary musical purposes, because Clayson & Garrett, after reinstating these balance points during their painstaking restoration of 1976–8, found it necessary to retain the lead in the jacks. The need to weight the jacks so heavily strengthens the supposition that the keyboard is unoriginal.

9 Harpsichord

Jacob Kirckman, London, 1762

The 1762 Jacob Kirckman harpsichord showing the handsome 'bookmatched' walnut veneer panels on the CHEEK and facia.

Opposite: The soundboard rose, photographed from the keyboard end. The rose is of the second design used by Kirckman. See entries nos.16 and 6 respectively for the first and third designs.

This DOUBLE-MANUAL harpsichord made by Jacob Kirckman (the founder of the firm) offers similar musical resources to the instrument of 1777 by him and his nephew Abraham (no.6): the left-hand pedal operates the MACHINE STOP in the same manner, though the right-hand pedal operates not a swell, but the BUFF STOP, which is now disconnected from its manually operated lever. Despite having been heavily restored internally, this instrument retains its handsome exterior walnut panels (compare with the fate of the 1752

Kirckman no.16), which are characteristic of the period before mahogany came into fashion. Fortunately, the authentic gilt ROSE, which is of Kirckman's second design, survives, albeit embedded in an unoriginal soundboard. The BRIDGES, NUTS and all the JACKS, save those of the LUTE REGISTER, are also modern replacements dating from various twentieth-century interventions.

The instrument, having reached its present condition, perhaps now offers better information and insight into early and mid-twentieth-century attitudes, expectations and restoration practices than those of the second half of the eighteenth century.

Maker Jacob Kirckman

Date and place 1762, London

Nameboard inscription
Jacobus Kirckman Londini fecit 1762

Other inscriptions
i   On the back of the name batten:
    Restored by Douglas Brown, Ewell 1951.
ii On the back of the name batten:
    Dolmetsch 1956 C.L.C.W. [Leslie Ward].

Case materials and dimensions
Oak, veneered with panels of walnut, crossbanded with mahogany, lines in boxwood. Length 2335, width 922, depth 300.

Compass *FF–f'''*, no *FF♯*

3-octave span 485 (both keyboards)

Disposition

←4'	lower keyboard
8'→	lower keyboard
←8' dogleg	lower and upper keyboards
←8' lute	upper keyboard
buff to 8'→	lower keyboard

Six hand stops with turned brass knobs, controlling the above registers and the machine stop; two pedals: the right one operates the buff stop (which is disconnected from its manually controlled lever) and the left one operates the machine stop. When the machine stop is engaged and the pedal is up, the lower manual sounds all three sets of strings and the upper sounds the front 8'. With the pedal depressed, the lower manual sounds the back 8' and the upper, the lute stop.

Stringing and scaling
Two sets of 8' strings and one 4'

	←8'			8'→		4'	
	string length	dogleg pluck point	lute pluck point	string length	pluck point	string length	pluck point
f'''	144	48	15	141	64	70	47
c'''	188	56	19	185	74	92	53
f''	270	69	22	263	85	135	60
c''	355	78	26	344	94	178	65
f'	541	91	29	523	106	272	70
c'	717	102	31	700	116	355	76
f	985	118	39	973	132	495	84
c	1214	131	44	1187	145	626	89
F	1492	150	53	1471	164	800	96
C	1652	165	62	1638	180	908	102
FF	1744	184	73	1737	200	1043	108

Bridges and nuts are not original and there are no string gauge numbers.

Present pitch *a'* = 440 *Hz*

10 Clavichord

Arnold Dolmetsch, Haslemere, 1925

Right: Arnold Dolmetsch in Haslemere, c.1925, seated at a clavichord. This resembles, in every visible detail, the one now at Fenton House and may indeed be the same instrument. Dolmetsch is surrounded by his family; from left to right: Mabel, Carl, Cécile and Nathalie. Cécile later married Leslie Ward and became a Keeper of the Benton Fletcher Collection at Fenton House (see App. II).

Above: Lid and keywell, showing the lid motto and nameboard inscription.

The Dolmetsch family workshop produced many clavichords like this one. It possesses the same struck action and range of expressive effects as the anonymous German instrument (no.19), but is unfretted, that is, each note has its own pair of strings (see Fig.3). The SOUNDBOARD decoration was done in egg tempera by Dolmetsch's wife, Mabel, in the style of the antique keyboard instruments which had passed through their hands. The French motto inside the lid, '*Plus fait douceur que violence*' means 'More is achieved through gentleness than violence'[1].

Arnold Dolmetsch (1858–1940) played a pioneering role in the twentieth-century revival of interest in early music and performances on period instruments. He was among the first to produce many instruments previously regarded as obsolete, from viols and recorders to harpsichords. As a prolific builder and energetic restorer, he also exercised a powerful, and at times idiosyncratic, influence on the development of the early music movement in England. Many equally forceful personalities in the Arts and Crafts movement and in literary life were acquainted with Dolmetsch and his work, and on friendly terms with him[2].

During the late twentieth century Dolmetsch's influence came to be judged rather harshly. Not only did his new keyboard instruments embody prevalent nineteenth-century notions of progress, but – more injuriously in the long term – his restoration techniques combined an often excessive replacement or redesign of original material with an almost complete lack of documentation[3]. Nevertheless, these workshop practices reflected pervasive attitudes towards contemporary music-making and artefacts of the past. Had it not been for the interest and enthusiasm engendered by Dolmetsch, and the instruments he produced and restored, the early music revival in England would have reached a far narrower and less influential audience.

Not part of the original Benton Fletcher Collection, this instrument was presented to the National Trust in 1960 by Mrs Janet Leeper on condition that it be played. It had belonged to her aunt, Miss Dorothy Swainson, who may well have been 'the first professional clavichordist'[4]. She gave concerts in Russia, France and Switzerland, as well as England, and remained a lifelong friend of Dolmetsch after their first meeting in Paris in 1911, at which he introduced her to the instrument. She edited the journal of the Dolmetsch Foundation for the twelve years preceding her death in 1959.

◉ CD track 17

1 A lid motto (in Latin) was a common decorative feature of Ruckers harpsichords and virginals.
2 For example, William Morris, Ezra Pound and Bernard Shaw were acquainted with Dolmetsch's work and supported it. See Dolmetsch, 1957, and Campbell, 1975.
3 While some interventions were milder than others and preserved original parts and dispositions, none were documented. Thirteen of the instruments in this collection alone have the signature or stamp of Leslie Ward, a leading member of the Dolmetsch firm (see Appendix I).
4 Campbell, 1975 p.184. But the honour might equally have been claimed by a contemporary of Miss Swainson: Violet Gordon Woodhouse, a sometime member of the Dolmetsch circle who was, by all accounts, an enthralling performer on both harpsichord and clavichord. She also led a colourful private life keeping four men in thrall in a *ménage à cinq*.

Maker Arnold Dolmetsch

Date and place 1925, Haslemere

Nameboard inscription
Arnold Dolmetsch anno MCMXXV

Other inscriptions
i On left-hand side case liner: Arnold Dolmetsch, Haslemere, Dec. 23. 1925 [handwritten in ink].

Case materials and dimensions
Walnut. Length 1125, width 375, depth 136

Compass C–d'''

3-octave span 474

Stringing and scaling
The instrument is unfretted, with bichord stringing throughout the compass. Longer string measured. Strings may be original.

	Bridge to tangent (sounding length)	Bridge to hitchpin
d'''	101	205
c'''	112	233
f''	165	326
c''	223	404
f'	341	530
c'	453	638
f	604	796
c	697	905
F	830	975
C	912	1002

Design pitch *a'* = 440 *Hz*
    resting at *a'* = 415.3 *Hz (awaiting repair)*

11 Virginals

Robert Hatley, London, 1664

The social turmoil of mid-seventeenth-century England spawned many lasting cultural effects. Deprived of the patronage of the monarchy and wealthy Royalist sympathisers, and subject to the strictures of a Puritan morality, musical entertainment during the Interregnum was significantly scaled down in dimension and extravagance[1]. In a context of both economic and moral stringency, a burgeoning of domestic music-making and of the indigenous production of the rectangular virginals so well suited to it, seems less remarkable.

This background may also help to explain why the English virginals continued to flourish, just as the popularity of the form was waning elsewhere in Europe[2]. The large majority of the 22 surviving examples span the period of the Civil War and Restoration. The earliest seventeenth-century example, an octave virginals by Thomas White, dates from 1638, and the last dates from about forty-five years later[3], by which time they were already being supplanted by the more compact wing-shaped spinets, of which the anonymous bentside spinet (no.7) is a comparatively late example. When Benton Fletcher acquired this virginals at auction in 1933, he distrusted the date on the jackrail, perhaps reasoning that an English virginals would have been made half a century or so earlier, when the vast English repertoire for virginals by William Byrd, Orlando Gibbons and their contemporaries was being composed. The enigma was resolved by later research, revealing that throughout the seventeenth century in England the word 'virginalls' signified plucked keyboard instruments of every type.

Perhaps as a concession to Puritan sensibilities, most of the extant examples have, like this instrument, sober, dark-stained oak cases. These betray no hint of their exuberant interiors, which, with their painted lids, applied gilt papers and decorated SOUNDBOARDS recall their Flemish antecedents, or of the coming English predilection for plain soundboards and veneered, panelled or natural wood exteriors. All seventeenth-century English virginals were made with vaulted lids, which also lent them, when closed, a rather sombre air. The lid of this virginals was flattened during the

Detail of the keywell with the facia removed, showing the jackrail inscription, the carved initials of the maker and the date 1664 on the keywell liner; to its right, the carved initials of the restorer 'TC' can be seen with the date 1732, and detectable in the light patch to the left, the handwritten name L. Ward. Also visible is the pair of drawers for music underneath the keyboard: a unique feature of this virginals. The keyboard is a twentieth-century replacement by Dolmetsch.

Opposite: Detail of a painted panel showing an early depiction in England of a tulip. This flower also recalls the English virginals' Flemish antecedents.

eighteenth century, perhaps by the person who left his initials, T.C., and the date 1732, neatly carved into the front surface of the keywell framing, beside the cruder ones of R[obert] H[atley] and the date 1664. The paintings on the lid and front flap depict figures in contemporary dress enjoying rustic surroundings. The apparent grotesqueries (e.g. the headless horseman, hunchbacked man) arise solely from the flattening of the lid.

Robert Hatley was a London virginals maker who resided in the parish of St. Giles Cripplegate[4]. This instrument, the only surviving example of his work, is in a remarkably good state. Although the keyboard and JACKS are twentieth-century replacements by Dolmetsch, some of the original materials were re-employed. A photograph predating this restoration confirms that its long compass is authentic[5], and that the key coverings were as they appear now: the NATURALS black, and the ACCIDENTALS, white. A unique feature of this instrument is the pair of music drawers underneath the keyboard, which significantly increases the case depth. The turned oak stand and the stool (which is not shown) are modern replacements[6], based on a rare original stand supporting a virginals by Thomas White dated 164(?)4 in Cardiff.

⊙ CD tracks 10–12

1   Domestic music-making was, paradoxically, the beneficiary of its expulsion from church and theatre. See Fraser, 1973.

2   Trade with the Netherlands was significantly disrupted during the Interregnum. In the Low Countries, late sixteenth- and early seventeenth-century production of virginals by the Ruckers family had been prolific and export to England was well established. However, the last surviving virginals by Couchet, Ruckers' brother-in-law, dates from 1650.

3   The 22 virginals include not only the 19 instruments listed in Boalch, 3/1995, p.714, but also the 1638 Thomas White octave virginals and the two late sixteenth-century virginals discussed by Martin, 2000. Neither of these is signed or dated, but they appear to be Elizabethan, from *c.*1580. The earliest surviving full-sized virginals from the seventeenth century dates from 1641, and the latest from 1684.

4   Boalch, 2/1974, p.64.

5   Only one surviving English virginals has a longer compass: that by Stephen Keene, 1668 (in the Russell Collection, Edinburgh) *FF-d'''* (no *FF♯*).

6   The stool and stand were made by Christopher Nobbs, based on drawings kindly supplied by Darryl Martin.

Maker Robert Hatley

Date and place 1664, London

Nameboard inscription
none

Other inscriptions
i   On the front of the jackrail: Roberttus Hatley Londini fecit 1664.
ii   On the keywell liner behind the facia: R.H. 1664 [carved].
iii   On the keywell liner behind the facia: TC 1732 [carved].
iv   On the keywell liner behind the facia: Arnold Dolmetsch Ltd., Haslemere, Surrey [stamped].
v   On the keywell liner behind the facia: L. WARD [stamped].
vi   On bottom board: Arnold Dolmetsch Ltd., Haslemere, Surrey [stamped].
vii   On bottom board: Leslie Ward 1950.
viii On the back of the facia: Repaired by Alec Hodsdon, Lavenham, Suffolk, June 1948.
ix   On the back of the facia: L. WARD [stamped].
x   On bass wrestplank capping: L. WARD [stamped].

Case material and dimensions
Oak, stained black with iron strap hinges. Lid originally vaulted, now flat.
Length 1675, width 522, depth 222.

Compass   *FF–c'''*, no *F♯*

3-octave span   474

Stringing and scaling
One set of 8' strings. The lowest jack faces towards the player.

	string length	pluck point
c'''	153	49
f''	208	49
c''	266	55
f'	378	53
c'	518	63
f	703	66
c	890	84
F	1112	93
C	1311	116
FF	1527	129

Present pitch *a'* = 409 *Hz*

12 Square Piano

John Broadwood, London, 1774

Above: Engraving of John Broadwood, aged 79. By W. Say, from an 1811 portrait by John Harrison.

Right: This instrument was acquired at auction in March 1980 by David Wainwright. As the hammer fell, it is reported that Stewart Broadwood (b.1931, great-great-great grandson of John Broadwood) said to him, 'Do you realise that that piano was owned by [A.J.] Hipkins?' Although the remark has been iterated orally, efforts to persuade Mr Broadwood to commit it to writing have proved fruitless.

The acceptance and popularity of the piano, the newly fashionable keyboard instrument with struck rather than plucked strings, was greatly abetted by the rectangular model known as the 'square'. Made in profusion by numerous builders in London from the 1760s onwards, this compact and inexpensive type of piano allowed players of every social rank to acquaint themselves with the potential of the new instrument and the growing body of repertoire demanding touch-sensitive dynamics. The squares were further promoted through use by the most famous composers of the period, including John Christian Bach, J.S. Bach's youngest son, who lived in London.

The action of this square piano (see Fig.5), a type of *Stossmechanik*[1], closely resembles that invented and perfected by Johann Zumpe (fl.1735–83), a former employee of Burkat Shudi. Among the first such actions to achieve widespread popularity, it was also widely imitated, not only by John Broadwood (who probably first met Zumpe in Shudi's shop), but also by Longman & Broderip, John Pohlman, Adam Beyer and many others working in London and abroad. Two manual stop levers to the left of the keyboard control damper-raising devices: one each for the bass and treble notes[2]. A BUFF STOP, operated by a now missing pedal, also formed part of the instrument's eighteenth-century disposition.

By 1774 John Broadwood had been managing the firm founded by his recently deceased father-in-law for at least three years. While both Shudi's and Broadwood's names continued to appear on harpsichords until 1793, the earliest surviving square pianos seemed to fall into a different category of enterprise; many lack both serial numbers and the founder's name.

Certainly one of the earliest surviving square pianos by Broadwood[3], this instrument was acquired by David Wainwright at the auction in March 1980 at which many of the instruments of the Broadwood Collection became dispersed[4]. He bequeathed the piano to Fenton House, where it has been exhibited since August 1999[5].

1 Cole, 1998 p.383 defines *Stossmechanik* as the term in modern German literature to signify those actions in which the hammers are not connected to the key but are mounted on a rail or other structure, the force impelling the hammer towards the strings being supplied by some moving agent activated by the key pushing or knocking the hammer.
2 The compass divides between *b♭* and *b♮*.
3 If genuine, then perhaps the earliest. A slight doubt must, however, remain over the authenticity of the inscription on the nameboard. The inscription is not centred in the available space and there is a distinct loss of clarity on the right-hand side of the central cartouche. In addition, the marquetry panels on either side of the central cartouche do not match exactly. Whether this is an 'innocent' consequence of over-exposure to light, other damage or fraudulent reworking, is unclear.
4 The SOUNDBOARD of the piano was replaced during its subsequent restoration by Tony Chappell. Photographs by Kenneth Mobbs, kindly donated to National Trust archives, show various details of this restoration.
5 This piano takes the place of the undated Christopher Garner square which never formed part of the original Benton Fletcher Collection, although displayed with it since the late 1940s at Cheyne Walk. It moved to Fenton House with the rest of the collection in 1952 and is now on show at Blickling Hall (Norfolk), where it is to be preserved (unplaying) for purposes of study.

Maker John Broadwood

Date and place 1774, London

Nameboard inscription
Johannes Broadwood Londini fecit 1774

Other inscriptions
none

Case materials and dimensions
Solid mahogany, inlaid with lines of boxwood and ebony: a diagonal striped pattern framed by broad dark and thin light parallel lines. Spine of softwood. Length 1467, width 488, depth 188.

Compass FF–f'''

3-octave span 485

Action
English single action, after Zumpe (Fig.5). Two hand stops with turned brass knobs to the left of the keywell, controlling damper-lifting mechanisms, one for the notes from FF–b♭, the other for the notes b–f'''. Pedal-operated buff stop [pedal now missing].

Stringing and scaling
Bichord throughout

	string length	strike point
f'''	105	23
c'''	144	26
f''	225	33
c''	299	32
f'	446	38
c'	563	46
f	724	53
c	838	56
F	1002	63
C	1117	68
FF	1295	82

There are no string gauge numbers.

Present pitch under reduced tension, awaiting repair.

13 Grand Piano

Inscribed Americus Backers, London, late 1770s

The post-Second World War stand has two pedals: the left operates the una corda (soft), and the right lifts the dampers (sustain).

Unlike most of his London contemporaries, Americus Backers eschewed square pianos and concentrated on producing grands. A Dutch immigrant working in Jermyn Street, Piccadilly, from 1763 until his death in 1778, he developed and perfected the so-called English action for grand pianos, which was reproduced by Broadwood, Longman & Broderip, Stodart and others (see Fig.6). Among the features he introduced, which later became standard on English pianos, were triple stringing (i.e. three strings for each note), damper and una corda pedals, and an action adjustment mechanism controlling the set-off point[1], which could be reached without removing the action[2]. This piano, like the Broadwood (no.14) of some 30 years later, possesses all these features.

Benton Fletcher was given this instrument by Dr and Mrs Fenn of Alston Court, Stoke-by-Nayland, Suffolk, where, he was told, it had stood ever since it was made[3]. He therefore believed it to be not only a genuine Backers, but also the earliest grand piano to be made in England. This distinction actually belongs to an earlier and clearly genuine Backers which has since come to light, signed and dated 1772 and now in the Russell Collection, Edinburgh.

Although wholly credible, the nameboard inscription is fraudulent.

In comparison with it, the Benton Fletcher piano must be judged a contemporaneous forgery. Backers's considerable success in London had made him an attractive target for the fraudulent activities of less prominent, although perhaps no less accomplished, rivals[4]. Documentary confirmation that his name was being applied to instruments not of his manufacture appears in his angry notice in the *Morning Post* of 14 April 1775, which warns the public to beware of counterfeits. This instrument is undoubtedly a case in point: the craftsmanship is of a good standard, although unfortunately the action has been much overhauled and the original SOUNDBOARD and BRIDGES have been replaced. The signatures on the keyboard merely add to the enigma: 'Grays No. 7' on the top key and a less legible one on the bottom key, which seems to read 'G. ...ady'[5]. It is not known whether Robert Falkener, the notorious forger of Kirckman harpsichords during the 1770s, also made counterfeit pianos or had a hand in this one[6].

1   In the English grand action (see Fig.6), the hammer is propelled towards the strings by an escapement lever (called the hopper) which releases the hammer before it reaches the strings (the momentum already imparted by the player's finger takes the hammer the rest of the distance to the strings), so that after the hammer has struck the strings, it falls away (or recoils) allowing the strings to vibrate freely. The set-off point is the hammer's distance from the strings at the moment when it is released from the hopper on a very slow depression of the key.

2   Cole, 1998, pp.118–19.

3   Ford, 1976, p.10. In a conversation about this article, Mr Ford said that the information concerning the provenance of this piano was given to him by the late Edward Croft-Murray, former Keeper of Prints and MSS at the British Museum, a collector of antique harpsichords and one of the early members of the Benton Fletcher Committee.

4   Cole, 1998, pp.114–28, collates and cogently relates what is known of Backers. This counterfeit Backers is also discussed: p.314.

5   Cole, 1998, p.125, interprets this as '...yer', perhaps belonging to Adam Beyer, but I believe this is a misreading. An undated photograph of the keyboard (removed from the instrument) in the National Trust archives shows the inscription more clearly than it appears today, but it is still quite small and indistinct. Magnified, it appears to read, 'G. [or possibly J.] C(?)ady.' Robert and William Gray (plausibly 'Grays', or even 'Gray's') made spinets for Longman & Broderip, and pianos, harpsichords and organs on their own account in London around 1793. It may be that one of them was subcontracted to provide action parts or was being apprenticed in the counterfeiter's shop at the time of this piano's manufacture.

6   In this regard, it is even more unfortunate that the original soundboard has been replaced: Falkener signed his own name on the underside of the soundboard in his 'Kirckmans'. This discreet location would be visible only if the bottom of the instrument were removed.

Maker unknown

Date and place late 18th century, London

Nameboard inscription
Americus Backers Londini fecit

Other inscriptions
i   On the top key: Grays No. 7.
ii On the bottom key: G.[or possibly J]...C[?]ady [?].
iii On the back of the facia: Repaired Aug 1948 by Alec Hodsdon, Lavenham, Suffolk [handwritten in ink].
iv On the back of the facia: Repaired June 1959 by Thomas N. Cooke [possibly 'Coole'], Beckenham, Kent.

Case materials and dimensions
Oak, veneered with mahogany panels and crossbanding, boxwood and ebony lines: a 'sandwich' with thick ebony between two thin lines of boxwood. Length 2068, width 944, depth 287.

Compass   FF–f'''

3-octave span   488

Action
English grand action, much altered
Two pedals. Left: una corda. Right: sustain (lifts dampers)

Stringing and scaling
Trichord throughout. Longest string measured.

	string length	strike point
f'''	101	11
c'''	137	9
f''	207	13
c''	279	19
f'	417	33
c'	554	46
f	841	70
c	1078	87
F	1422	116
C	1536	139
FF	1589	168

There are no string gauge numbers.

Present pitch Detensioned. To be retained (unplaying) for study.

14 Grand Piano

John Broadwood & Son, London, 1805

The stand is original and has two pedals: the left operates the una/due cordae (soft), and the right lifts the dampers (sustain), as in the Backers (no.13).

Not part of the original Benton Fletcher Collection, this piano was first sold from Tebaldo Monzani's shop in Old Bond Street to Philip Wyckam of Thame Park[1]. The instrument remained in the Wyckam family home until about 1900, when it was sold to Robert Green. His daughter, Mrs Corbett Dyer, gave the instrument to the National Trust in 1954 and it was first displayed at Hughenden Manor, before being moved to Fenton House in 1959.

In most respects a typical English grand piano of the late eighteenth and early nineteenth centuries (see Fig.6), it is triple strung throughout its five-and-a-half octave compass from *FF* to *c''''*,[2] and has two pedals. One of these, as on a modern piano, lifts the DAMPERS. The other realigns the action laterally so that the hammers strike only one string out of every trichord. A wooden slip stop in the treble key-endblock can be engaged (pushed down) so that the realignment allows two out of every three strings to be struck[3]. Many of these features, including the ability to adjust the hammer set-off point without removing the action, were introduced at least 30 years earlier in the grand pianos of Americus Backers, who is credited with developing the English grand action (see no.13).

This instrument was produced during a period of rapid, indeed almost frantic, expansion for the Broadwood firm. John Broadwood had recently retired, leaving his sons James Shudi and Thomas in charge. As well as illustrating the technical skill and well-nigh perfect craftsmanship that had become a commonplace in instruments of this quality in England, it embodies the scientific approach to construction, string tension and striking

point that was Broadwood's principal contribution to piano design. In musical terms, his rational refinements to Backers's basically sound concepts resulted in a greater evenness of tone, as well as increased dynamic flexibility and volume[4].

🔘 CD tracks 15–16

1   My thanks are due to David Hunt for supplying this information about the piano from the Broadwood Archives. Monzani was an Italian flautist, music publisher and flute and clarinet maker, who lived and worked in London from *c.*1785 until his death in 1839. In Holden's Triennial [Trade] Directory of 1805–7 he appears as 'Monzani & Cimador, musical instrument makers and music sellers to the Prince of Wales, 3, Old Bond St.' From 1808 onwards he worked in association with the instrument maker Henry Hill, under the name Monzani & Co. (Langwill, 6/1980, and Kreitzer, 1995).

2   This compass, with an extended half octave in the treble, had been available from Broadwood's since 1789, when it was first requested by the composer and pianist Jan Ladislav Dussek. See Wainwright, 1982, p.75.

3   It is unclear whether the default position of this wooden slip is up or down. In a five-and-a-half octave Broadwood grand of 1792, described by Dahl and Barnes, 1997, pp.208–11, an original label glued behind the nameboard suggests that the small slip of wood is ordinarily in its down position but drawn upwards to facilitate tuning.

4   Adlam, 1972.

Maker   John Broadwood & Son

Date and place   1805, London

Nameboard inscription
1805, John Broadwood and Son, Makers to His Majesty and the Princesses, Great Pulteney Street, Golden Square, London

Other inscriptions
i   On the wrestplank: No. 3251 [handwritten in ink].
ii   On the keybed: Lacoch 3263.
iii   On middle C key: Peter Redstone 1961.
iv   On a printed label fixed on the back of the facia: Adlam Burnett, Historical Keyboard Instruments Ltd., Registered Office: Finchcocks, Goudhurst, Kent TN17 1HH, Tel: Goudhurst (05803) 451.
v   Handwritten in pencil on the above label: Restored 1975. Further work carried out 1984 Derek Adlam [signed].
vi   On the treble edge of the fallboard: 3251 [stamped].
vii   On a label affixed to the bottom boards under the keywell: 110, Fenton House.

Case materials and dimensions
Oak, veneered on all sides (including spine) with mahogany panels and crossbanding, lines in boxwood. Length 2251, width 1052, depth 293.

Compass   *FF–c''''*

3-octave span   487

Action
English grand action (see Fig.6). Hand stop: in right-hand key-end block, wooden slip for limiting the lateral movement of the keyboard when the pedal is depressed, allowing the player to choose between creating due corde or una corda when down or up respectively. Two pedals. Left: una corda or due corde depending on the position of the hand stop. Right: sustain (lifts dampers).

Stringing and scaling
Trichord throughout. Divided bridge, breaks between G♯ (last brass string) and A (first steel string). All three strings for each note have the same sounding lengths. String lengths were measured when the instrument was unstrung.

	string length	pluck point
c''''	70	6
f'''	99	10
c'''	134	14
f''	204	21
c''	274	31
f'	412	48
c'	548	66
f	823	99
c	1101	127
F	1268	143
C	1550	153
FF	1724	172

There are no string gauge numbers.

Present pitch   *a'* = 415.3 *Hz*

15 Harpsichord

Anonymous, Italian, *c.*1590

This rare single-strung harpsichord escaped the fate of many similar instruments that came to be fitted with one or more additional sets of strings or even pedal boards[1]. Fewer than 20 such unaltered examples now exist. Fortunately, this instrument also retains its original JACKS and keyboard, complete with its divided or split ACCIDENTALS in the bass. The distal portion of each of these keys sounds the expected chromatic note, while the proximal portion sounds a more frequently used low bass note (see SHORT OCTAVE). The exact disposition of the bass notes is drawn below.

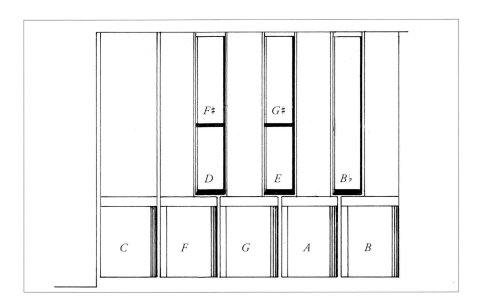

Fig. 10 The disposition of the divided or split accidentals in the bass of this harpsichord. Compare with Fig.9, the conventional C/E short octave, p.46. The keys are labelled as they sound.

Made atypically from walnut rather than the more usual cypress, the instrument is also one of the few in the collection with an old, although probably not original, stand. The richly painted outer case, from which the relatively lightly built instrument can be completely withdrawn, has also survived. This very common type of construction, known as a 'true' inner-outer case, contrasts with the 'false' inner-outer construction of the Celestini virginals in the North-West Attic (no.18).

72

The delicate rose is made of circular layers of parchment cut into lace-like geometric patterns.

The present external case painting, although very early, is probably not the original, which was green, surrounded by a yellow stripe and a red border[2]. The lid interior (see p.30) depicts Moses and Aaron, who is turning his staff into a snake, before the Pharaoh (Exodus VIII:10–11), who is flanked by his magicians and Egyptian soldiers (in the garb of Roman legionaries) in a Tuscan landscape. The delicate ROSE has the three-dimensional form of an inverted wedding cake suspended from the SOUNDBOARD down into the instrument. There used to be a carved cherub, presumably symmetrical with the remaining one at the bass end of the keyboard, at the treble end.

Keywell showing the single remaining cherub and the original keyboard with divided or split accidentals in the bass. (See also p.2.)

The TIMBRE of this harpsichord, often regarded as quintessentially Italian with its incisive attack and comparatively quick decay, ideally suits not only a vast continuo repertoire, but also a large body of solo music from the late sixteenth and early seventeenth centuries. Toccatas, ricercares, suites and fantasias, some with very daring harmonic progressions, were composed with instruments like this in mind by such Italian masters as Frescobaldi, Gabrieli, Rossi and their contemporaries and successors.

CD tracks 25–26

1   Not to say that it has escaped every vicissitude. During one of its early twentieth-century restorations the soundboard was completely removed by the expedient of sawing around its case edge. A skilful and painstaking restoration by Clayson and Garrett in 1976 rectified the damage, and relieved the instrument of many twentieth-century accretions.
2   This evidence is from a National Trust restoration report dated 10 January 1979. However, an earlier report dated 13 January 1975 from the Courtauld Institute, where it was sent for x-ray, suggests that the original decoration was blue or blueish green streaked with white in a 'marbling' pattern.

Maker Unknown

Date and place *c.*1590, Italy

Nameboard inscription
none

Other inscriptions
i   On the back of the facia: Repaired by Alec Hodsdon, Aug. 1948, Lavenham, Suffolk [handwritten in ink].
ii On the back of the facia: Repaired by Arnold Dolmetsch Ltd., Haslemere Surrey. 1950 Leslie Ward [signed].

Case materials and dimensions
Walnut with soundboard of straight-grained softwood. All dimensions exclude mouldings and outer case. Length 1876, width 790, depth 239.

Compass and disposition
C/E, short octave – *c'''*. Accidentals *F♯* and *G♯* are divided so the front portions of those keys sound the diatonic notes *D* and *E* respectively, while the rear portions sound the accidentals (see Fig.10). One non-movable 8' register.

3-octave span   511

Stringing and scaling
One set of strings

	←8'	
	string length	pluck point
c'''	154	52
f''	228	75
c''	293	90
f'	422	111
c'	566	126
f	832	126
c	1148	126
F	1375	126
C/E	1436	126

There are no string gauge numbers.

Present pitch *a'* = 409 *Hz*

16   Harpsichord

Jacob Kirckman, London, 1752

One of the earlier surviving harpsichords by Jacob Kirckman (the earliest dates from 1744), this is among the very few with only two sets of 8' strings (see also the Longman & Broderip, no.17), both operated by manual stop levers. Possessing neither a MACHINE STOP nor even a BUFF STOP, it is, mechanically, the simplest English harpsichord in the collection. The ROSE is of Kirckman's earliest design.

The instrument's first owners are unknown, but some time during the nineteenth century its original external walnut veneer was covered or, more likely, replaced with the present satinwood and maple, which had become more fashionable. By the time of its showing at the International Inventions Exhibition of 1885 (at which, coincidentally, two other harpsichords in the collection, nos 1 and 2, were also shown) it again belonged to the Kirckman firm. This is confirmed in the very terse entry in the *Guide to the Loan Collections*, which gives no additional identifying information[1]. In 1896 the Kirckman firm was taken over by Collard & Collard. It may have been at around this time that the instrument passed into the hands of the restorers Dyson & Son of London and Windsor, whose label appears above the nameboard[2]. Sold at Puttick & Simpson's in 1929 to a buyer identified only as 'Bolton', it reappeared in the auction rooms in 1934 when it was acquired by Benton Fletcher.

Opposite: Soundboard rose, photographed from the keyboard end. The rose is of the first design used by Kirckman. See entries nos 9 and 6 respectively for the second and third designs.

◉ CD tracks 8–9

1 Hipkins, 1885. The *Guide* has a slightly more expansive introduction by Hipkins.
2 During its 1983 restoration, pieces of card supporting this view were found under the keyboard. These pieces comprise parts of tickets or invitations to a function to be held on a Saturday in December 1897 at the Albert Institute in Windsor. Taken together with the workman's initials and the date of 1898 on the lowest key, this provides a basis for the conjecture that the harpsichord was in Dyson's Windsor workshop in 1897–8. I am indebted to Andrew Garrett for supplying all the details of this evidence.

Maker Jacob Kirckman

Date and place 1752, London

Nameboard inscription
Jacobus Kirckman fecit Londini 1752

Other inscriptions
i   On a label on the front of the facia: Restored by Dyson & Sons, London & Windsor.
ii On the wrestplank: L. Ward [stamped].
iii On the back of the name batten: L. Ward [stamped].
iv On the back of the name batten: Restored by A. Dolmetsch Ltd., Haslemere 1950, C.L.C. Ward [signed].
v   On the lowest key: [indecipherable initials, perhaps AUR] 1898.

Case materials and dimensions
Oak, now veneered with light coloured panels, crossbanding and lines in maple and satinwood; originally veneered in walnut, as evidenced by the string- and keywells. Length 2282, width 921, depth 275.

Compass *FF–f'''*, no *FF♯*

3-octave span 484

Disposition One keyboard
  8'→
  ←8'

Two hand stops with turned brass knobs, controlling the above registers. Originally left knob controlled the front 8' and the right knob, the back 8'. Now the left knob controls the back 8' and the right, the front 8'.

Stringing and scaling
Two sets of 8' strings

	←8'		8'→	
	string length	pluck point	string length	pluck point
f'''	131	55	126	71
c'''	172	61	169	78
f''	259	73	252	89
c''	346	80	336	97
f'	521	95	504	111
c'	694	105	671	120
f	977	121	952	137
c	1193	134	1166	151
F	1462	154	1443	170
C	1639	168	1619	185
FF	1799	187	1787	207

String gauge numbers are written in ink in modern numerals on the 8' nut between the pairs of strings for the indicated note.

8'	
between the pair of strings for	gauge no.
c''	4 [nearly obliterated]
b'	5
c'	5
b	6
f♯	6
f	7
c	7
B	8
F♯	8
F	9
D	9
C♯	10
BB	10
BB♭	11
AA	11
GG♯	12
GG	12
FF	13

Present pitch *a'* = 415.3 *Hz*

17 Harpsichord

Longman & Broderip, London, 1783

Opposite: The stand is post-Second World War, and the pedal operates the machine stop.

In common with many harpsichords with the names Longman & Broderip on the nameboard batten, this instrument was actually made by Thomas Culliford, working for the music publishers and instrument dealers on a commission basis. Culliford, having worked for John Hitchcock, set up his own workshop in London and built a variety of keyboard instruments, both by himself and in partnership with others. Of the various freelance keyboard instrument makers who also worked for Longman, the best known was Baker Harris.

Showing distinct entrepreneurial flair throughout his long career, James Longman first set up business in Cheapside in 1767 and was joined two years later by a Mr Lukey. In 1775 Francis Broderip was taken into partnership, and shortly thereafter Lukey withdrew. The firm continued as Longman & Broderip, trading from premises both in Cheapside and Haymarket until 1798, when the partnership went bankrupt. Longman's business was revived during the nineteenth century with, among other partners, the composer, piano maker and pianist Muzio Clementi. The firm survived into the twentieth century, but eventually, like the descendants of Shudi and Kirckman, was subsumed by a trading subsidiary of Yamaha, in this case Chappell.

Front of the name batten, with the misspelling of the word 'Instrument', and the back of the batten showing Thomas Culliford's signature, address, date and numbering, as well as, on the far left, the signature of Leslie Ward (of Dolmetsch). See technical data for complete wording of inscriptions.

Longman & Broderip's business card. Note the incentive to seafaring merchants and other potential agents: 'Large Allowance for Merchant Captains of Ships & others who take for Sale'.

Apparently found beneath two large armchairs in a secondhand shop in Wells, Somerset, this harpsichord may have been Benton Fletcher's first acquisition. Its musical disposition with only two 8' REGISTERS and a BUFF STOP is curiously simple considering its late date. Probably even later, in an attempt to equip the instrument with the means to play piano music, a rudimentary pedal-operated MACHINE STOP was added. This device, in keeping with the aesthetic ideal of the late eighteenth-century English harpsichord, facilitates the largest possible dynamic and timbral contrast with the available resources (see technical data).

◉ CD track 21

Maker Thomas Culliford

Date and place 1783, London

Nameboard inscription
Longman and Broderip, Musical Instument
[*sic*] Makers, No. 26, Cheapside and No. 13
Haymarket, London

Other inscriptions
i   On the back of the name batten: No.
    14 [or 11].
ii On the back of the name batten: No.
    234, Thos. Culliford Maker, Fountain
    Court Cheapside London, March, 1783.
iii On the back of the name batten: No.
    14 [followed by an indecipherable word
    or initials, resembling CAORLD].
iv On the back of the name batten:
    Requilled 1971 Sept., C.L.C. Ward,
    Haslemere.
v   On the wrestplank: L. Ward [stamped].

Case materials and dimensions
Oak, veneered with mahogany panels,
walnut crossbanding and maple or holly
lines. Length 2162, width 913, depth 279.

Compass   *FF–f'''*, no *FF♯*

3-octave span   488

Disposition   One keyboard
        8'→
        ←8'
buff to 8'→

Two hand stops with turned brass knobs.
One pedal operating the machine stop
which is permanently engaged. Only the
back 8' knob controls its register; the
front 8' is held in its on position all the
time by the machine stop spring and can
only be withdrawn by pedal. The back 8'
must be engaged manually for the machine
stop to work correctly. When the pedal is
up, the two 8' registers sound together;
when depressed, the front 8' is withdrawn
and a buff stop is engaged on the back 8'
which sounds alone.

Stringing and scaling
Two sets of 8' strings

	←8'		8'→	
	string length	pluck point	string string	pluck point
f'''	135	51	137	79
c'''	175	59	169	76
f''	259	71	249	87
c''	345	81	331	96
f'	517	94	496	109
c'	677	104	652	120
f	939	122	911	137
c	1148	135	1119	149
F	1430	154	1404	169
C	1609	169	1589	184
FF	1717	187	1711	206

String gauge numbers are stamped on the 8' nut between the pairs of strings for the
indicated note.

8'	
between the pair of strings for	gauge no.
f'''	4
c♯''	4
c''	5
c♯'	5
c'	6
f♯	6
f	7
c♯	7
c	8
A	8
F♯	8
F	9
D	9
C♯	10
C	11
BB	11
BB♭	12
AA	12
GG♯	13
GG	14
FF	15

Present pitch *a'* = 415.3 Hz

18 Virginals

attributed to Giovanni Celestini, Venice,
late 16th or early 17th century

A very rare instrument, this unsigned double strung virginals, now attributed
to Giovanni Celestini, was evidently found by Benton Fletcher in a cellar in
Florence where, being used as a carpenter's workbench, he had to 'brush out
the shavings to see inside'. It may also have the distinction of being, as Major
Fletcher claimed in several articles[1] and in a radio programme of 29
September 1938, the first virginals to have been played on television, in a
broadcast from Alexandra Palace. It is now one of the few keyboard
instruments in the collection that is not in playing condition.

Little is known of Giovanni Celestini except that he worked in Venice
between 1583 and 1610, producing harpsichords and virginals, several of
which are extant. This instrument bears close similarities to a signed example
of 1594 in the Museum für Kunst und Gewerbe in Hamburg, which also has
two rather than the more usual single string for each note. Important features
shared by the two instruments include: the ability to disengage one of the 8's

ROSE viewed from the keyboard end.

for purposes of tuning or to create a dynamic contrast (between one 8' and two 8's), nearly identical key-cheek designs, similar mouldings, and a half-recessed keyboard. Only the Fenton House example, however, has a false inner-outer case. Unlike the majority of contemporary Italian virginals, which, like the Hamburg Celestini (and the Siculus and Vincentius, nos 4 and 5) were lightly built and meant to rest within highly decorated and robust wooden outer cases from which they could be withdrawn, this instrument has thicker, integral case walls with deceptive cap mouldings designed to give an impression of the usual type of construction[2].

1 For example, 'Early Music at Old Devonshire House', *The Listener*, 6 October 1938, p.714.
2 In fact, the false impression is so strong that earlier guidebooks to this collection state that the instrument was once removable from its outer case and came to be fixed into it during a (misguided) restoration. It is now clear that this instrument was originally made as it stands now: as a false inner-outer case double-strung virginals. I am indebted to Grant O'Brien for clarifying this point, for discovering and bringing to my attention the many close similarities of the Hamburg instrument to this one, and for suggesting – on the basis of as yet unpublished evidence – this wholly credible attribution. I am also grateful to Denzil Wraight who, while agreeing that an attribution to Celestini is preferable, has pointed out several strong similarities to features of instruments by Donatus Undeus, a keyboard instrument maker from Bergamo, fl.1590–1623.

Detail of the left key CHEEK, *the profile of which is nearly identical to that of the Celestini in Hamburg.*

Maker Giovanni Celestini

Date and place late 16th or early 17th century, Venice

Nameboard inscription
none

Other inscriptions
none

Case materials and dimensions
Integral (false inner/outer) case. Painted softwood [?] faced on the interior with cypress. Length 1512, width 668 (excluding the half-recessed keyboard, 736 including it), depth 215.

Compass   C/E–f''', short octave

3-octave span   503

Disposition
One keyboard, two 8's
No hand stops or pedals. Keyboard may once have been movable, in order to engage or disengage the jacks for the second set of strings for purposes of tuning and/or to allow a dynamic contrast between one 8' and two 8's.

Stringing and scaling
Two sets of 8' strings. Lowest jack faces away from the player.

	Longer 8'		Shorter 8'	
	string length	pluck point	string length	pluck point
f'''	116	69	116	67
c'''	148	67	146	64
f''	223	70	221	66
c''	300	80	297	75
f'	451	114	446	109
c'	597	160	592	156
f	863	254	853	248
c	1059	300	1051	295
F	1220	243	1215	242
C/E	1235	231	1232	230

There are no string gauge numbers.

Present pitch Detensioned. To be retained (unplaying) for study.

19 Clavichord

Anonymous, German, late 17th or early 18th century

Unlike harpsichords, spinets and virginals, which have plucked strings, those of the clavichord are struck by TANGENTS (see Figs 3 and 11). Using the direct contact with the string that this action affords, the player can produce not only touch-sensitive dynamics, but also such expressive effects as vibrato (also known as *Bebung*) and the *Tragen der Töne*[1], impossible on any other keyboard instrument. In the late eighteenth century in Germany, composers developed a special notation to indicate the use of these effects on the clavichord. In compact instruments like this one, a single pair of strings

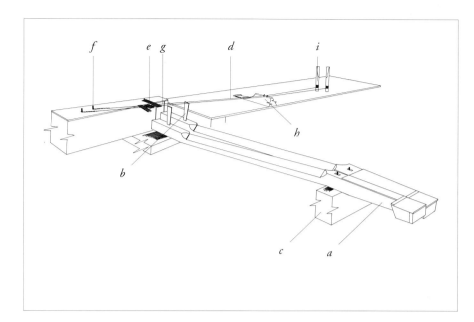

Fig. 11 *The action of a fretted clavichord. The two keys and tangents share one set of strings. The tangents simply strike at different points along the string set, creating two different notes. The listing damps (silences) the untuned portion of the string (the overlength, from hitchpin to tangent) and also the sounding portion, once the tangent has left the strings.*

a key
b tangent
c balance rail
d string pair, tuned portion
e listing
f hitchpin
g string pair, overlength
h bridge
i tuning pin

struck by the tangents at different points along its sounding length serves for two, three or (more rarely) four adjacent notes. Such an arrangement is called 'fretting' and is shown above.

The fretted clavichord, although not particularly rare, is of great historical significance, both for its widespread use throughout the sixteenth, seventeenth and early eighteenth centuries, and for its remarkable versatility. These modest-looking instruments served many functions: for domestic music-making, as practice organs and harpsichords, as compositional and didactic aids and even, as iconographic evidence suggests, to accompany recorders, lutes or transverse flutes. During the eighteenth century, fretted clavichords were gradually superseded by the unfretted type, of which the Dolmetsch clavichord (no.10) is a relatively modern example.

The fretting system employed in this anonymous clavichord is shown fully in the technical data overleaf. There is a SHORT OCTAVE arrangement identical with that on the Siculus virginals (no.4).

◎ CD tracks 13–14

1 *Bebung* or vibrato is produced by repeatedly increasing and decreasing the pressure on the depressed key while the note is still sounding. The *Tragen der Töne* is akin to the bowing technique on the violin, known as portato, in which several notes taken in a slur are slightly separated. Achieving the same slurred-yet-detached effect on the clavichord involves the 'swelling' of the sound of consecutive individual notes by increasing the pressure on the key. The resulting rise in pitch is perceived as an increase in volume.

Maker Unknown

Date and place late 17th or early 18th century, Germany

Nameboard inscription

Other inscriptions

i   On back of facia: repaired by Alec Hodsdon, Lavenham, F=P 1948 [possibly 1943].

ii On back of facia: L. WARD 1950 [stamped].

iii On back of facia: 1970 LW [carved].

iv On the top key (key no. 45): P[aul] N[eville].

Case materials and dimensions

Possibly walnut. Length 1055, width 308, depth 107.

Compass   *C/E–f'''*, short octave

3-octave span   *F–e''*: 487; *c–b''*: 484

Present pitch   *a'* = 415.3 *Hz*

Stringing and scaling

The instrument is fretted, with bichord stringing throughout the compass. In each octave the three notes *d–e♭–e* share a single pair of strings, as do *f–f♯–g*, *g♯–a–b♭* and *b–c–c♯*. Each of the lowest bass notes (*C/E–A*) has its own pair of strings, while the next four bass notes (*B♭*, *B*, *C* and *C♯*) are double, rather than triple fretted.

String pair	note	Bridge to tangent (sounding length)	Bridge to hitchpin
20	*c'''*	119	382
↓	*b''*	128	↓
19	*b♭''*	135	424
↓	*a''*	144	↓
↓	*g♯''*	152	↓
18	*g''*	157	466
↓	*f♯''*	166	↓
↓	*f''*	174	↓
17	*e''*	182	509
↓	*e♭''*	193	↓
↓	*d''*	204	↓
16	*c♯''*	213	554
↓	*c''*	222	↓
↓	*b'*	237	↓
15	*b♭'*	243	598
↓	*a'*	257	↓
↓	*g♯'*	273	↓
14	*g'*	280	645
↓	*f♯'*	297	↓
↓	*f'*	313	↓
13	*e'*	323	692
↓	*e♭'*	342	↓
↓	*d'*	363	↓
12	*c♯'*	374	743
↓	*c'*	394	↓
↓	*b*	421	↓
11	*b♭*	434	794
↓	*a*	460	↓
↓	*g♯*	489	↓
10	*g*	504	832
↓	*f♯*	533	↓
↓	*f*	563	↓
9	*e*	572	844
↓	*e♭*	605	↓
↓	*d*	640	↓
8	*c♯*	656	854
↓	*c*	685	↓
7	*B*	701	862
↓	*B♭*	729	↓
6	*A*	747	870
4	*G*	792	885
2	*F*	833	895
5	*E/G♯*	770	878
3	*D/F♯*	813	890
1	*C/E*	855	899

Restorers and Repairers of the Benton Fletcher Collection

Appendix I

All the names listed below are arranged in chronological order as far as possible and, except for the last three, appear on instruments of the collection, written either directly on instrument parts or on labels affixed to nameboards. The workshops of Clayson & Garrett (Lyminge, Kent), David Hunt (Willingham, Cambs) and Miles Hellon (Greenwich, London) listed last, left no identifying marks, but provided documentation about the work they undertook. An asterisk denotes that the work of restoration or repair has been documented with a written report, which remains in National Trust files.

T.C.
1732   Hatley virginals, 1664 (no.11)

Henry John Dale, Cheltenham, Glos
1882   Shudi & Broadwood harpsichord, 1770 (no.1)

Dyson & Sons, London and Windsor, Berks
*c.*1898   Kirckman harpsichord, 1752 (no.16)

Charles Hersant, 49 Lennox Road, Stroud Green Road, N. London
(no legible dates,   Shudi & Broadwood harpsichord, 1770 (no.1)
prob. early 1900s)   Shudi harpsichord, 1761 (no.3)

Henry Tull, 3 Leopold Road, Ealing Common, London
1938   Ruckers harpsichord, 1612 (no.2)

Alec Hodsdon, Lavenham, Suffolk
1948, June   Hatley virginals, 1664 (no.11)
    August   'Backers' grand piano, late 1770s (no.13)
    August   Anonymous single-strung Italian harpsichord, *c.*1590
                (no.15)

Anonymous German fretted clavichord, late 16th or
early 17th century (no.19)

'Hancock' English bentside spinet, late 18th century (no.8)

Leslie Ward, Arnold Dolmetsch Ltd., Haslemere, Surrey

1950	Unsigned English bentside spinet, first half of 18th century (no.7)
1950	Kirckman harpsichord, 1752 (no.16)
1950	Shudi harpsichord, 1761 (no.3)
1950	Anonymous single-strung Italian harpsichord, *c.*1590 (no.15)
1950 & 1970	Anonymous German fretted clavichord, late 17th or early 18th century (no.19)
1950	Hatley virginals, 1664 (no.11)
1951	Shudi & Broadwood harpsichord, 1770 (no.1)
1956	'Hancock' English bentside spinet, late 18th century (no.8)
1956	Kirckman harpsichord, 1762 (no.9)
1957	Siculus virginals, 1540 (no.4)
1970	Ruckers harpsichord, 1612 (no.2)
1971	Longman & Broderip harpsichord, 1783 (no.17)
n.d.	Kirckman harpsichord, 1777 (no.6)

Douglas Campbell-Brown, Ewell, Surrey

1951	Ruckers harpsichord, 1612 (no.2)
	Kirckman harpsichord, 1762 (no.9)

Thomas N. Cooke (or possibly 'Coole'), Beckenham, Kent

1959, June	'Backers' grand piano, late 1770s (no.13)

Peter Redstone

1961	Broadwood grand piano, 1805 (no.14)

John Barnes, Edinburgh

1969	Shudi harpsichord, 1761 (no.3) *

Adlam/Burnett, Finchcocks, Goudhurst, Kent
1975   Broadwood grand piano, 1805 (no.14) *
                    Kirckman harpsichord, 1777 (no.6) *

Tony Chappell, Bristol
*c.*1980   Broadwood square piano, 1774 (no.12) (then owned by
                    David Wainwright)

Derek Adlam, Welbeck, Notts
1984   Broadwood grand piano, 1805 (no.14) *

Richard Clayson and **Andrew Garrett**, Lyminge, Kent (and **Paul Neville**
[PN]**, an assistant in the workshop)
1973–4   Single-strung Italian harpsichord, *c.*1590 (no.15) *
1974   Shudi & Broadwood harpsichord, 1770 (no.1) *
1978   'Hancock' English bentside spinet, late 18th century
                    (no.8) *
1979   Anonymous German fretted clavichord, late 17th or
                    early 18th century (no.19), done by PN *
1980   Kirckman harpsichord, 1762 (no.9) *
1983–4   Shudi & Broadwood harpsichord, 1770 (no.1) *
1983   Kirckman harpsichord, 1752 (no.16) *
1984   Ruckers harpsichord, 1612 (no.2) *
1984   Vincentius virginals, late 16th or early 17th century
                    (no.5) *

David Hunt, Willingham, Cambs
1996   Broadwood square piano, 1774 (no.12) (then owned by
                    David Wainwright) *
1997   Broadwood grand piano, 1805 (no.14) *

Miles Hellon, Greenwich, London
2000–2001   Anonymous English bentside spinet, first half of 18th
                    century (no.7) *

Appendix II Previous Keepers of the Benton Fletcher Collection

By 'Keeper' we mean the person who deals with the practical day-to-day matters of tuning and replacing strings and plectra. The individuals who have held this post have had almost unlimited access to the instruments during their tenure at the collection. Their actual work may have ranged from tuning and minor maintenance to complete overhaul. The dates before 1973 are approximations. It is likely that the routine maintenance of instruments was carried out by more than one person concurrently during the period when the collection was at Cheyne Walk and in the early years at Fenton House. Records of routine maintenance before 1984 are few and sketchy.

Irvin Hinchcliffe
Acquisition–*c.*1947(?)   Old Devonshire House/Cheyne Walk

John Sebastian Morley, harp maker of 56 Old Brompton Rd, SW7
From *c.*1946   Cheyne Walk

Robert Arnold, an American.*
From *c.*1948   Cheyne Walk
to *c.*1957   Fenton House

Cécile Ward (*née* Dolmetsch, Arnold and Mabel Dolmetsch's daughter who married Leslie Ward in 1925) and, on occasion, **Leslie Ward**
Post–1952   Fenton House
to *c.*1973

Lionel Box, of 3 Upper Park Road, Bromley, Kent (the pianos only)
1965–1971   Fenton House

Kenneth E. Wilson of Wembley, Middlesex. (the pianos only, at three monthly intervals)
1971–1973(?)   Fenton House

Cécile and Leslie Ward and Ian Harwood

early 1970s   Fenton House4

Maurice Cochrane

1973–1984   Fenton House

Donald Mackinnon and Mimi Waitzman

1984–1996   Fenton House

Mimi Waitzman

1996–present   Fenton House

Information provided by Lorna Arnold, personal correspondence, 19 August 1994.

Appendix III Transcript of Handwritten Letter from Benton Fletcher to the Friends of Music Society (see page 10)

Old Devonshire House,
48 Devonshire Street, Theobald's Road,
  W.C.1
Telephone: Holborn 7043
April 12 1937

Dear Madam Benenson,

<u>Friends of Music, London.</u>

    You were kind enough to invite me to become a patron of the Friends of Music. In return for the honour I can offer my large music room (to seat nearly 50 persons) for occasional concerts with the use of two harpsichord and early virginals, but beyond this I can promise only to advertise the doings of the Society by placing notices in this house, which, as you know, is open to students & others interested in early keyboard and chamber music. If this offer be acceptable my name can be added to the Society's patrons for I feel it an honour to be associated with the Friends of Music.

    I trust that the Society will hold meetings, when required, at my house, for it is my hope to increase the work associated with my scheme for the revival of ancient music. The inclosed [*sic*] letter (which please return) will explain the ~~proposed~~ [crossed out] additional interest, which, it is proposed to inaugurate when I regain possession of the ground floor suite of rooms. Not only Handel, but also all the British Composers up to about 1800 are to be included in the museum. With the help of musicians & others, this long neglected memorial to our great men might grow into something worthy of our heritage. It is not to be a dead museum of glass cases, but, a living institution with performances of music & lectures upon kindred subjects. If the 'Friends of Music' have no headquarters of their own & are in sympathy with the developement [*sic*] of my scheme perhaps a meeting ~~might~~ [crossed out] could be arranged here in which our common interests might be discussed with mutual advantage? I should be glad to hear from your Society on the subject if you think fit to bring it forward? I am anxious to form a Committee for collecting articles, prints & portraits for exhibition etc.

Yours sincerely,
[signed:] Benton Fletcher

I have written a short history of Old Devonshire House which is to be published in the Coronation number of 'Country Life' on April 17th with nine illustrations which show some of the musical collection instruments here.

Glossary

Accidentals. The notes which are termed 'flat' or 'sharp' and are respectively a half step (semitone) below or above the associated NATURAL note. The black notes on the conventional piano keyboard.

Balance pin. See BALANCE RAIL.

Balance rail. The keys of a keyboard are fitted onto a frame which holds them in place laterally, but allows them to move up and down on pins which act as fulcra. The balance rail is the centre section of that frame into which these balance pins are driven. See Figs 1, 3, 7 and 8.

Bentside. The side of a HARPSICHORD, SPINET or PIANO case which is curved.

Bridge. On stringed keyboard instruments, the long thin curved wooden structure on the SOUNDBOARD, over which the strings pass and into which pins are fixed. The strings bear against the pins, which thus determine one of the two endpoints of the sounding lengths of the strings. The bridge is the medium through which the vibrations of the strings are transmitted to the soundboard. See also NUT.

Buff (or **Harp**) **stop.** On instruments of the harpsichord family, a series of cloth or leather pads which, mounted on a sliding wooden batten positioned against the distal side of the NUT, can be moved into contact with the sounding lengths of each of the strings on a given register. When plucked by the PLECTRUM in the normal way, the string thus yields a less percussive and more muffled sound than that produced without the use of the stop (see Figs 8 and 9). The device is also found on some early pianos (e.g. Broadwood square piano, no.12).

Cheek. The case side of a harpsichord adjoining the BENTSIDE at the keyboard end, to the right of the keyboard. The term 'cheekpieces' may also refer to the case sides to either side of the keyboard, that is, also including that part of the SPINE to the left of the keyboard.

Clavichord. A keyboard instrument, usually rectangular in shape, in which the strings are struck by TANGENTS, upright blades of metal mounted in the distal ends of the keys. See Figs 3 and 11 and instrument nos 10 and 19.

Damper. The agent by which a sound is silenced. Harpsichord dampers (see Fig.1) were usually made of woollen cloth; piano dampers, of leather, cloth or felt (see Figs 4, 5 and 6). The non-sounding length (or overlength) of a clavichord string is damped by cloth called LISTING (see Figs 3 and 11), which is woven among the strings.

Dogleg coupler. The mechanism favoured by late eighteenth-century English harpsichord makers that allows the simultaneous playing of two sets of strings at normal pitch from the lower keyboard. The means by which this is accomplished is the dogleg jack, which has a piece cut out from its proximal edge, allowing it to be lifted by a key on both the upper and lower keyboards. See Fig.8.

Dynamics. The volume, that is, the loudness or softness of sounds.

Eight-foot pitch. Normal pitch (see Author's Note).

Four-foot pitch. An octave above normal pitch (see Author's Note).

Harp stop. See BUFF STOP.

Harpsichord. In modern terminology, a keyboard instrument with a plucked action possessing both a BENTSIDE and strings parallel to the keyboard.

Intabulation. A transcription of a musical piece into diagrammatic notation or tablature, rather than conventional notation. Tablature notation arises from a depiction of a specific instrument's string and/or key layout and relies for its correct interpretation on the consistency of that instrument's string/key layout and tuning.

Jack. The mechanism at the heart of the action of instruments of the harpsichord family. A rectangular slip of wood standing upright on the back (distal end) of the key, it holds a pivoted TONGUE, which acts as an escapement and which in turn holds fast the PLECTRUM. See Figs 1, 2, 7 and 8.

Lid swell. See NAG'S HEAD SWELL.

Listing. See DAMPER. See also Figs 3 and 11 in which the listing is labelled.

Lute register. A row of JACKS which, because of its position very near the NUT, produces a distinctly nasal sound. The lute register could, on the upper keyboard of a typical late eighteenth-century English double-manual harpsichord, have been heard on its own or in contrast with the back 8' register with or without the 4'. See Shudi & Broadwood harpsichord, 1770 (no.1); Kirckman harpsichord, 1777 (no.6); and Kirckman harpsichord, 1762 (no.9), and see Fig.8.

Machine stop. On English harpsichords, ordinarily a pedal-operated device which can usually be engaged or disengaged by means of a manual stop lever located in the case side to the left of the keyboard. When engaged, it allows the registration of the instrument to be changed instantaneously at the touch of a pedal, ie without the player's hands having to move from the keyboard to a hand stop lever or from one keyboard to the other. Usually consisting of forged iron parts, it is often concealed in a narrow wooden box fixed to the outer SPINE side of the harpsichord. The mechanism may also occupy the hidden space behind the facia directly above the keyboard(s) and is linked to the pedal by a thin metal rod which passes through the keyboard(s) and bottom boards. An integral part of the aesthetic of English harpsichords, it provides for maximum contrast quickly and easily within the instrument's given resources. See instrument nos 1, 3, 6, 9 and 17.

Manual (double, single). Another word for keyboard. Single-manual instruments have one keyboard; double-manual ones have two.

Nag's head or **Lid swell.** A device often found on late eighteenth-century English harpsichords (See Kirckman harpsichord, 1777 (no.6)) in which the section of the lid of the instrument which covers the stringwell is divided and hinged along a line roughly parallel with the straight portion of the BENTSIDE. The portion of the lid bordering the bentside can then be raised and lowered by means of a pedal in order to create crescendo (opening the lid) and diminuendo (closing the lid) or loud and soft. A mechanically simpler version of the VENETIAN SWELL.

Naturals. The counterpart to ACCIDENTALS. They correspond to the white notes on the conventional piano keyboard and are named A, B, C, D, E, F and G.

Nut. The long thin wooden structure into which the pins that guide the strings are fixed, thus determining one of the two endpoints of the sounding lengths of the strings. The other endpoint is determined by the pins driven into the BRIDGE. On a harpsichord, spinet or piano, the nut is positioned on the WRESTPLANK; in virginals, it is positioned in whole or in part on the soundboard. See Figs 7 and 8.

Piano (also **Pianoforte** or **Fortepiano**). A keyboard instrument in which the strings are struck by hammers and in which the loudness of the sound is controlled by the force of the player's touch. The term fortepiano is often used today to denote pre-modern pianos, but was used in the eighteenth and nineteenth centuries interchangeably with the words pianoforte or piano.

Plectrum. The agent by which a string is plucked in instruments of the harpsichord family. It is made of the centre shaft of a bird's feather, or from leather. Modern harpsichords often employ a synthetic substitute for quill called Delrin®. See Figs 1 and 2, and JACK and TONGUE.

Ravalement. A French term (for which there is no English equivalent) derived from the verb *ravaler* (figuratively to disparage, reduce, or run down, but also to consume or swallow up). It thus aptly reflects the process by which seventeenth-century Flemish harpsichords were enlarged, engulfed or changed by eighteenth-century French and other European harpsichord makers to suit eighteenth-century musical purposes (see Ruckers harpsichord, no.2).

Register. On a harpsichord, spinet or virginals, a row of JACKS. Large English harpsichords can have four registers of jacks (see Fig.8), while spinets and virginals usually have a single register. Also the name for the wooden batten which holds the jacks upright and aligned over the keys. The register is often movable so that the jacks which it guides can be engaged (made to sound) or disengaged by means of a connection with a manual lever or pedal.

Registration. The REGISTER or combination of registers selected by the player of a harpsichord or organ.

Rose. The circular ornamental design, often including the initials or other identifying mark of the maker, set into a similarly shaped hole in the soundboard of a keyboard instrument. Neither hole nor ornament is thought to serve any acoustical purpose.

Short octave. A disposition of the keys in the bass which makes the more commonly used diatonic notes (or NATURALS) available in the bass in place of the rarely needed ACCIDENTALS. In one such arrangement, which was exceedingly common throughout the sixteenth and seventeenth centuries, the lowest key, apparently the note E, actually sounds C. Similarly, the apparent F♯ sounds D, and the G♯ sounds E. See the Siculus virginals, (no.4); single-strung Italian harpsichord (no.15); Celestini virginals (no.18); and German fretted clavichord (no.19), and see Fig.9.

Soundboard. The acoustical heart of a stringed keyboard instrument. The very thin plank of wood visible beneath the strings, often made from knot-free quarter-sawn softwood such as fir or spruce, or, especially in Italian instruments, from slab-sawn cypress. Soundboards of French and Flemish harpsichords were frequently decorated with painted flowers, fruits, birds and arabesques.

Spine. The long straight side of a harpsichord or piano; on a spinet, virginal or clavichord, the side opposite the keyboard.

Spinet. In modern terminology, a plucked keyboard instrument in which the NUT is mounted on the WRESTPLANK, the longest string is the one furthest from the player, and the tuning pins are arrayed along the front of the case. See instrument nos 7 and 8.

Stops. On keyboard instruments, the various REGISTERS and additional mechanical devices for creating special effects available to and controlled by the player. See also BUFF STOP and MACHINE STOP.

Tail. The shortest side of a harpsichord case, furthest from the keyboard, joining the BENTSIDE with the SPINE.

Tangent. The thin blade of metal fixed in an upright position on the distal end of a clavichord key. The part of the clavichord action which, when a key is depressed, strikes the string, causing it to sound, and at the same time defines one of the string's endpoints. The other endpoint is determined by the BRIDGE. See Figs 3 and 11.

Timbre. Quality of tone or tone colour. The aspect of a sound which is neither its pitch nor its loudness.

Tongue. The pivoted part of a jack, which holds fast the PLECTRUM and acts as an escapement, allowing the plectrum to return beneath the string after having plucked it. See Figs 1, 2, 7 and 8, and JACK.

Venetian swell. A pedal-operated device patented by Shudi in 1769 for creating dynamic gradation or contrast. It is an inner lid consisting of a series of louvered panels or shutters. Opening and closing the shutters by depressing and releasing the pedal slowly, creates crescendo and diminuendo; if done quickly it creates loud and soft. See Shudi & Broadwood harpsichord, 1770 (no.1). (See also NAG'S HEAD SWELL).

Virginals. In modern terminology, a plucked keyboard instrument in which the NUT and BRIDGE are mounted in whole or in part on the soundboard, in which the longest string is the one nearest the player and the tuning pins are located along the side (usually the right side) of the case. See instrument nos 4, 5, 11 and 18.

Wrestplank. The part of the structure of a stringed keyboard instrument into which holes are drilled to hold the tuning pins. Of robust dimension, sometimes laminated but usually made of a single plain-grained slab of hardwood such as oak, beech, walnut or sycamore, it is designed to support the considerable tension exerted by the strings, despite its perforations. See Figs 7 and 8.

Bibliography

Adlam, Derek, Unpublished remarks for the National Trust on the 1805 Broadwood grand piano (1972).

Bach, C.P.E., *Essay on The True Art of Playing Keyboard Instruments,* translated and edited by William J. Mitchell (W.W. Norton & Co.: New York, 1949).

Barclay, Robert L., ed., *The Care of Historic Musical Instruments,* (Museums & Galleries Commission, Canadian Conservation Institute and CIMCIM: Edinburgh, 1997).

Bingham, Tony, ed., *Patents for Inventions, Abridgements of Specifications Relating to Music and Musical Instruments AD 1694–1866* (facsimile of second edition, 1871, Tony Bingham: London, n.d.).

Blom, Eric, ed., *Grove's Dictionary of Music and Musicians* (Macmillan: London, 5/1954).

Boalch, Donald, *Makers of the Harpsichord and Clavichord 1440–1840,* (George Ronald: London, 1956; Clarendon Press: Oxford, 2/1974; ed. Charles Mould, Clarendon Press: Oxford, 3/1995).

Brauchli, Bernard, *The Clavichord* (Cambridge University Press: Cambridge, 1998).

Burney, Charles, *Music, Men and Manners in France and Italy 1770,* edited by H. Edmund Poole (Eulenberg Books: London, 1974).

Campbell, Margaret, *Dolmetsch: The Man and his Work* (Hamish Hamilton: London, 1975).

Cole, Michael, *The Pianoforte in the Classical Era* (Clarendon Press: Oxford, 1998).

Colles, H.C., ed., *Grove's Dictionary of Music and Musicians* (Macmillan: London, 3/1927).

Dahl, Bjarne and John Barnes, 'Changes in English Grand Piano Actions between 1787 and 1792', *Galpin Society Journal*, Vol. L, March 1997, pp. 208–11.

Dale, William, *Brief Description of Spinets, Virginals, Harpsichords, Clavichords and Pianos, Shown in the Loan Collection of the International Inventions Exhibition* (Fargues & Co.: London, [1885]).

Dale, William, *Tschudi: The Harpsichord Maker* (Constable & Co.: London, 1913).

Denton, Pennie, ed., *Betjeman's London* (John Murray Ltd.: London, 1988).

Dolmetsch, Mabel, *Personal Recollections of Arnold Dolmetsch* (Routledge & Kegan Paul Ltd.: London, 1957).

Fletcher, George Henry Benton, copy of a transcrip with annotations in his own hand of his radio broadcast of 29 September 1938.

Fletcher, George Henry Benton, 'Early Music at Old Devonshire House', *The Listener*, 6 October 1938, pp.713–14.

Fletcher, George Henry Benton, *Old Devonshire House* (The National Trust: London, 1938).

Fletcher, George Henry Benton, Old Devonshire House: The New Music Centre, Reprinted from the *Amateur Musician*, 1939.

Forbes, Elliot, ed., *Thayer's Life of Beethoven* (Princeton University Press: Princeton, NJ, 1970).

Ford, Augustine, 'The Benton Fletcher Collection of Musical Instruments', *National Trust Magazine*, No.26, Autumn 1976, p.10.

Fraser, Antonia, *Cromwell: Our Chief of Men* (George Weidenfeld & Nicolson: London, 1973).

Fraser, Antonia, *King Charles II* (Weidenfeld & Nicolson: London, 1979).

Guy, John, *Charles I and Oliver Cromwell* (Ticktock Publishing: London, 1998).

Harding, Rosamond, *The Piano-Forte: Its History Traced to the Great Exhibition of 1851* (Cambridge University Press: Cambridge, 2/1978).

Hess, Albert G., 'The Transition from Harpsichord to Piano', *Galpin Society Journal*, Vol. VI, July 1953, pp.75–94.

Hipkins, A.J., *Guide to the Loan Collections and List of Musical Instruments, Manuscripts, Books, Paintings and Engravings* (Wm. Clowes & Sons: London, 1885).

Hubbard, Frank, *Three Centuries of Harpsichord Making* (Harvard University Press: Cambridge, Mass., 1965).

Hunt, David, Unpublished reports for the National Trust on the 1805 Broadwood grand piano (1997) and the 1774 Broadwood square piano (2000).

Kirkpatrick, Ralph, *Domenico Scarlatti* (Princeton University Press: Princeton, NJ, 1953).

Koster, John, *Keyboard Musical Instruments in the Museum of Fine Arts, Boston* (Boston Museum of Fine Arts: Boston, 1994).

Kreitzer, Amy, 'Serial Numbers and Hallmarks on Flutes from the Workshop of Monzani and Hill', *Galpin Society Journal*, Vol. XLVIII, March 1995, pp.168–80.

Langwill, L.G., *An Index of Musical Wind-Instrument Makers* (Langwill: Edinburgh 6/1993).

Latham, Robert, ed., *The Illustrated Pepys: Extracts from the Diary* (Penguin Books: London, 1979).

MacTaggart, Ann, and Peter MacTaggart, 'A Royal Ruckers: Decorative and Documentary History', *Organ Yearbook*, Vol. XIV, 1983, pp.78–96.

Martin, Darryl, Unpublished remarks and technical data for the National Trust on the anonymous German clavichord (1999).

Martin, Darryl, Unpublished remarks and technical data for the National Trust on the Hatley virginals (1992).

Martin, Darryl, 'Two Elizabethan Virginals?' *Galpin Society Journal*, Vol. LIII, April 2000, pp.156–67.

Martin, Darryl, 'Tangent Layout and Triple-fretted Clavichord Tuning' *De Clavicordio IV*, Musica Antica a Magnano: Magnano, 2000.

Maunder, Richard, *Keyboard Instruments in Eighteenth-Century Vienna* (Clarendon Press: Oxford, 1998).

Murphy, Graham, *Founders of the National Trust* (National Trust Enterprises: Great Britain, 2002).

Nicholson, Hubert, 'A Living Museum of Old Music', *Bazaar Exchange and Mart*, Vol. CXXIX, No. 37, 14 September 1937.

O'Brien, Grant, *Ruckers: A Harpsichord and Virginal Building Tradition* (Cambridge University Press: Cambridge, 1990).

O'Brien, Grant, 'The Use of Simple Geometry and the Local Unit of Measurement in the Design of Italian Stringed Keyboard Instruments: An Aid to Attribution and to Organological Analysis' *Galpin Society Journal*, Vol. LII, April 1999, pp.108–71.

O'Brien, Grant, Unpublished remarks and technical data for the National Trust on the Celestini virginals (1995).

Pollens, Stuart, *The Early Pianoforte* (Cambridge University Press: Cambridge, 1995).

Russell, Raymond, *The Harpsichord and Clavichord* (Faber & Faber: London, 1959; revised by Howard Schott, Faber & Faber: London, 2/1973).

Russell, Raymond, *Catalogue of the Benton Fletcher Collection of Early Keyboard Instruments at Fenton House, Hampstead* (Country Life for the National Trust: London, 1957, 1969, 1976; as *A Catalogue of Early Keyboard Instruments: The Benton Fletcher Collection at Fenton House*, with revisions by Trevor Pinnock and Andrew Garrett, (National Trust: London, 1981); with revisions by Trevor Pinnock, Andrew Garrett, and Mimi Waitzman (The National Trust: London, 1986 and 1991).

Sadie, Stanley, ed., *The New Grove Dictionary of Music and Musicians,* 20 vols. (Macmillan: London, 1980).

Sadie, Stanley, ed., *The New Grove Dictionary of Musical Instruments,* 3 vols. (Macmillan: London, 1984).

Voss, E(lizabeth) W., 'Harpsichords for the Amateur', *Amateur Musician,* December 1934.

Wainwright, David, *Broadwood by Appointment: A History* (Quiller Press: London, 1982).

Wainwright, David and Mobbs, Kenneth, 'Shudi's Harpsichords for Frederick the Great', *Galpin Society Journal,* Vol. XLIX, March 1996, pp.77–94.

Waitzman, Mimi S., 'From "Ancient Musicland" to Authenticity' *Music and Musicians,* Vol. XXXVII, No.3, November 1988, pp.17–22.

Waterhouse, William, *The New Langwill Index: A Dictionary of Musical Wind Instrument Makers and Inventors* (Tony Bingham: London, 1993).

Wells, Elizabeth, ed., *Royal College of Music Museum of Instruments Catalogue, Part II: Keyboard Instruments* (Royal College of Music: London, 2000).

Willis, Roy, 'Valediction' in the *West London Press* (?), July 25 1952, (no page number).

Wraight, Denzil, 'The Identification and Authentication of Italian String Keyboard Instruments', in *The Historical Harpsichord,* edited by Howard Schott (Pendragon Press: New York, 1992), Vol. III, pp.59–161.

Wraight, Denzil, and Christopher Stembridge, 'Italian Split-Keyed Instruments with Fewer than Nineteen Divisions to the Octave', *Performance Practice Review,* Vol. VII, No.2, 1994, pp.150–81.

Wrightson, Keith, *English Society 1580–1680* (Hutchinson: London, 1982).

Picture Credits

All technical drawings by Christopher Nobbs

All photographs by the National Trust/John Hammond
except as follows:
pages 14 (below), 68 (left): The National Trust
pages 9 (both), 12, 13 (right): Courtesy of Derek Jackson
page 13 (left): National Trust Photographic Library/Matthew Antrobus
pages 14 (above), 20, 61, 65 and 73: National Trust Photographic
    Library/Nadia Mackenzie
page 50: from a private collection, photograph by John Hammond.
page 74 (above): National Trust Photographic Library/John Bethell
page 60 (right): reproduced by kind permission of John Murray, London.
    Original photograph by Bernard Alfieri.
page 80: reproduced by kind permission of Tony Bingham, and
    photographed by John Hammond.

Index